Foreword

There used to be a time when video game enthusiasts could only experience the very best in places called "arcades".

In the early '90s, 16-bit home consoles such as the Super Nintendo, the Sega Genesis, or the NEC PC Engine were ramping up in terms of horsepower. However, they were a far cry from the hardware found in coin-operated "Amusement Machines".

Nicknamed "coin-ops", these cabinets ran video games featuring multitudes of huge sprites covering the whole screen, beautiful colors, digitized sounds, and engaging high quality music. These machines were in a league of their own.

Accessing arcades was an adventure in itself. Quarters had to be gathered, means of transportation acquired, and paper maps studied. Some carpooled while others used their bikes. Lucky ones had "amusement venues" dedicated to video games in their hometown while others found themselves in a dirty pub surrounded by adults who did not seem to have much magic happening in their lives.

Amount of play time was directly correlated with skill level. Coins were spent carefully, after having studied other people's techniques. The only certainty resulting from the expedition was a day ending with empty pockets.

Despite all these obstacles, video game connoisseurs found the attraction irresistible. Players of all ages and origins gravitated to the same places in order to follow their passion.

Rows of lined up cabinets created a highly competitive environment where publishers only had a few seconds to catch a player's attention and, most importantly, their quarters. It was during this time that a young company named Capcom managed to rise above the competition, seemingly producing one masterpiece after another, and turn itself into an icon.

The history of Capcom and the genesis of Street Fighter II, Ghouls 'n Ghosts, and Final Fight belongs in history books. Unfortunately when I started researching the topic, I found little to satisfy my curiosity and next to nothing about the engineering side of things.

The fierce rivalry between publishers warranted extreme secrecy. Artists, programmers, and designers were only credited with their nicknames in order to avoid poaching. As for the hardware powering Capcom's titles, nothing ever officially transpired except for a code name, **CP-System**.

This book attempts to shed some light on the mystery platform. It is an engineering love letter to the machine that enabled Capcom's tremendous success.

– Fabien Sanglard
Occasional Link to the Past

Sunnyvale, CA
November, 2022

Contents

3

Acknowledgments

Thanks to **Victoria Ho** for proofreading this book and avoiding grammatical carnage.

Thanks to **Loïc Petit** for generously sharing his expert knowledge of the CPS-1 and the CPS-2. The section about the CPS-A and CPS-B graphic ASICs would not have been possible without the extensive documentation he produced. He also volunteered to proofread the multiple drafts of this book and suggested many important improvements. His contribution was invaluable.

The other giant upon whose shoulders this book stands is **Upsilandre**. He spent a considerable amount of time explaining Pixel Aspect Ratio and spotted many mistakes during proofreading. He conducted and shared the results of much research not only on the CPS-1 but also on the X68000. He shared articles and a methodology for exploring Capcom ports on gamopat-forum.com that were particularly insightful.

Thanks to **Charles MacDonald** for sharing his knowledge of the CPS-1 and for patiently explaining and re-explaining the art of tile map circuitry.

Thanks to **Ben Torkington** for making available "SF2:Platinum", his ANSI C rewrite of "Street Fighter II: World Warriors".

Thanks to **STG** for his translation of Japanese articles on shmuplations.com.

Thanks to **VGDensetsu** for his numerous articles about the Street Fighter series and Japanese game development in general.

Thanks to **mvs-scans.com** for their high-quality photos of the CPS-1 boards.

Thanks for **John McMaster** for his high-res scans of the CPS-A ASIC.

Thanks to the **M.A.M.E contributors** for the extensive documentation work they produced over all these years. You guys are the unsung heroes of arcade history.

Thanks to **Mike Stedman** for shedding light on some of the X68000's most obscure features and ports.

Thanks to **James Young (Pronoiac)** for his extensive set of pull requests to improve the grammar of this book.

Reporting Issues

This book strives for accuracy. If you find mistakes, omissions, or typos, please take the time to report these issues.

Or even better, patch the book with a pull request since the full source code is available online on GitHub.

Report an issue: **https://github.com/fabiensanglard/cpsb/issues**.

Send a pull request: **https://github.com/fabiensanglard/cpsb/pulls**.

Send me an email: **fabiensanglard.net@gmail.com**.

Capacity Cheat Sheet

It is dangerous·to go alone. Many chips are studied in the hardware chapter. Counting the pins and inferring capacity can easily lead to "off-by-one" errors.

Take this.

Pins	Capacity KiA	Capacity Addresses	Pins	Capacity KiA	Capacity Addresses
1	–	2	17	128	131,072
2	–	4	18	256	262,144
3	–	8	19	512	524,288
4	–	16	20	1,024	1,048,576
5	–	32	21	2,048	2,097,152
6	–	64	22	4,096	4,194,304
7	–	128	23	8,192	8,388,608
8	–	256	24	16,384	16,777,216
9	–	512	25	32,768	33,554,432
10	1	1,024	26	65,536	67,108,864
11	2	2,048	27	131,072	134,217,728
12	4	4,096	28	262,144	268,435,456
13	8	8,192	29	524,288	536,870,912
14	16	16,384	30	1,048,576	1,073,741,824
15	32	32,768	31	2,097,152	2,147,483,648
16	64	65,536	32	4,194,304	4,294,967,296

Pins count truth table.

Introduction

The origin of Capcom can be traced back to the founding of two companies by Kenzo Tsujimoto: I.R.M. Corporation in 1979 and its subsidiary Japan Capsule Computers Co in 1981. Located in Osaka prefecture, the two companies manufactured and distributed electrical games.

After a merger in 1981 the resulting entity, Sanbi, was rebranded "Capcom" in 1983. The first medal cabinet[1], released the same year, was a baseball title named "Little League".

The nickname of their products, "**Cap**sule **Com**puters", summarized the values of the company. Intending to extend beyond the trendy personal computers of the era, the "coin-ops" were sold as "capsules packed to the brim with gaming fun". The hard outer shell embodied the desire to protect intellectual property and prevent illegal copies which were inferior imitations.

In 1984, Capcom entered the world of video games with their first title "Vulgus". Arcades were a competitive world where cabinets had only a few seconds to catch the eyes of a customer. It was especially difficult for a company which, at the time, did not have the best technology.

> I always considered Capcom as someone fighting with a bamboo stick. We didn't have the resources to equal Sega's or Namco's hardware.
>
> While they were racing in F1 cars, we were driving Hondas.
>
> — Noritaka Funamizu (a.k.a "Poo"), Capcom Game Planner[2]

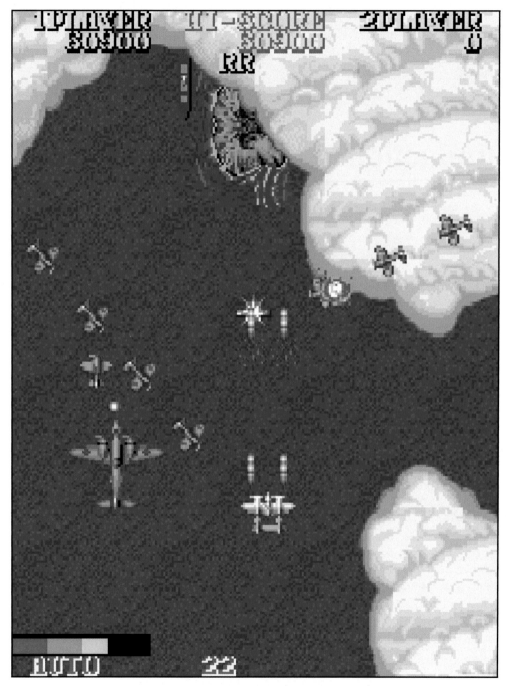

1943: The Battle of Midway by Capcom (1987)

The metaphor is justified when comparing two titles from 1987 side by side: Capcom's "1943" (which Poo directed) and Sega's "Afterburner".

Sega's platform, named "X Board", was in a league of its own. Its core ran on dual 12.5 MHz Motorola 68000 CPUs. The graphics processor, the Sega Super Scaler chipset clocked at 50MHz, was capable of both scaling and rotating up to 256 sprites, over two background layers, and one "road" layer.

Its sound system was powered by a 4MHz Zilog Z80 which drove a SegaPCM 16-channel stereo PCM chip. It allowed digitized music and sound far surpassing what could be achieved with the more common FM synthesis chips of the era.

In the opposing corner, Capcom's valiant board featured a 6Mhz z80 CPU with a graphics system capable of animating 32 sprites on top of one text layer and two background layers [3].

The sound system, piloted via a second z80 running at 3Mhz, generated both music and sound effects via Yamaha FM synthesis.

Afterburner by SEGA (1987)

Despite its simple graphics, 1943 sold honorably. It even managed to become the second highest-grossing table arcade game of 1987 thanks to its engaging gameplay.

The dawn of Capcom saw other titles that did well despite their limited technology. In 1985, "Wolf of the BattleField" (a.k.a Commando) conquered the world and particularly the UK where test locations resulted in orders totaling a thousand units[4].

Commando (1985)

USA distributor, Data East, prominently advertised the profitability!

Released in 1985, Ghost 'n Goblins is another video-game which is emblematic of Capcom's capacity to do more with less in its early days.

With the same "bamboo stick" technology used in Commando, and the same planner (Tokuro Fujiwara) directing a team consisting of programmer Toshio Arima, artist Masayoshi Kurokawa, and composer Ayako Mori, Ghost 'n Goblins was another hit.

In this medieval fantasy-inspired title, the hero is to rescue an abducted lover. Arthur must face hordes of Zombies, Magicians, Skeletons, Red Arremers, Flying Knights, and the most unforgiving control system known to mankind.

The story was well put together. Bosses such as Unicorns, Dragons, Satan, and the chief Astaroth were well-animated. Despite its nightmare-inducing difficulty, players liked the game.

Ghost 'n Goblins (1984)

It became the 10th highest-grossing arcade game in Japan and reached 9th in the US.

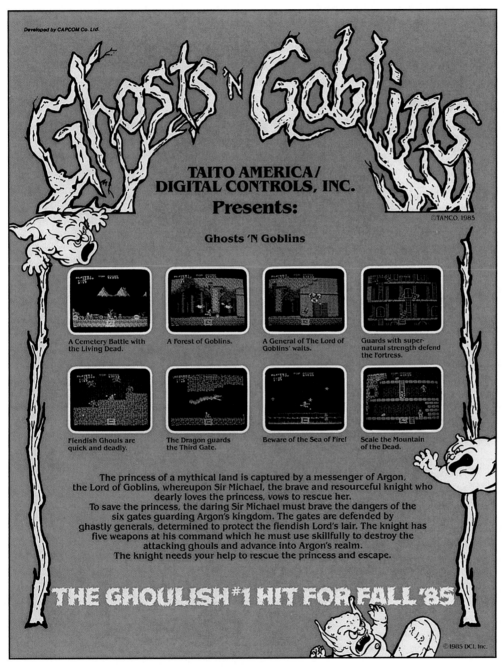

Ghost 'n Goblins flyer (1984)

What Capcom lacked in raw power, they made up with imagination and tinkering. But wit was not always enough. In 1987, Capcom published "Street Fighter", an audaciously innovative title but a commercial failure.

In "Street Fighter", players controlled their characters with a standard joystick but used two large pneumatic pushers for kicks and punches. Pipes conducted air to the board where pressure was measured. The harder a player punched the button, the higher the damage inflicted.

Without tactile feedback, players tended to smash as hard as possible, forgetting to manage their effort. After a few rounds the right arm was shot, and gameplay was no longer fun after fatigue set in. Besides enjoyment, there were also the issues of injuries and tendinitis. To rectify, Capcom retrofitted the control system with something more "standard" while still allowing players to select the power via six "normal" buttons.

The game became playable but doomed by unimpressive graphics and sluggish controls. The cabinet was largely ignored and despite attempts to boost sales with discounts, "the most amazing dedicated upright ever" soon fell into oblivion.

Street Fighter 1 (1987)

Street Fighter 1 cabinet flyer

1.1 Costly Production

Besides facing technologically superior competitors, Capcom had to deal with a constantly evolving production pipeline. Looking at the **P**rinted **C**ircuit **B**oards (PCBs) hosting their games from 1984 to 1988 reveals a high variation of components.

Summarizing Capcom's usage of the Motorola 6809, Zilog z80, Motorola m68k, Intel 8751 (MCU), YM2203, YM2151, YM2149, and MSM5205 in a table shows that even titles produced the same year wouldn't necessarily feature the same chips.

Even the ubiquitous z80 was used inconsistently since it could be dedicated to game logic, audio, or both, like in the "1942" board, which features two of them.

Game Name	Year	M6809	z80	m68k	i8751	2203	2151	2149	5205
Vulgus	1984		X					X	
Higemaru	1984		X					X	
1942	1984		X					X	
Commando	1985		X			X		X	
Ghost 'n Goblins	1985	X	X			X		X	
Gun Smoke	1985		X			X		X	
Section Z	1985		X			X		X	
Trojan	1986		X			X			X
Speed Rumbler	1986	X	X			X	X		
Dyn Side Arms	1986		X			X	X		
Legendary Wings	1986		X			X	X		
1943	1987		X			X	X		
Black Tiger	1987		X		X	X	X		
Street Fighter	1987		X	X	X		X		X
Tiger Road	1987		X	X		X	X		X
Bionic Commando	1988		X	X	X		X		
F1-Dream	1988		X	X	X	X	X		

Usage of chips in Capcom arcades from 1984 to 1988 [18].

Even though games did mostly the same thing (move sprites over backgrounds), the hardware had to be re-invented over and over again.

This constant evolution slowed production since game programming pace was hindered by bugs in the hardware. Full speed could only be achieved in the later stages of development which placed Capcom at a further disadvantage.

1.2   Plagued by Piracy

Since Capcom's PCBs were made with off-the-shelf components, counterfeiters where able to copy them, dump the software ROMs and build replicas called "bootlegs".

Without having to offset the cost of development, these copies sold for less than official games. The missed sales weighed heavily on Capcom's financial health.

1.3   Capcom NT (New Technology)

Production difficulties, competition, and piracy painted an uncertain future for Capcom's arcade division. As history would have it, they not only survived, but thrived.

A new era began in 1988. Forgotten Worlds and Strider gave players their first glimpse into what the Osaka company was now capable of producing.

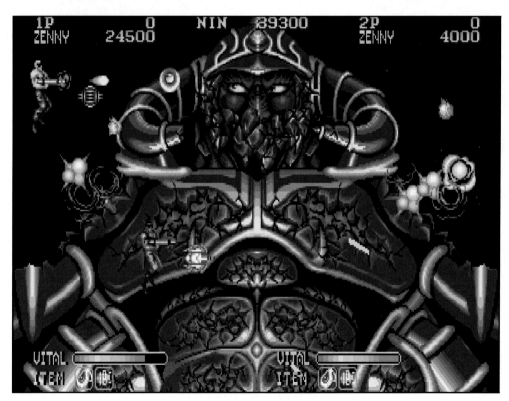

Forgotten Worlds (1988)

Capcom's CPS-1 announcement flyer (1989)

With both games using a mysterious "new technology" (later renamed **CP-System** and **CPS-1**), production quality was greatly improved. Massive sprites moved on the screen. They were made of many more colors on top of several layers simulating parallax. Levels were more elaborate (Strider had impressive climbable sloped surfaces). The audio improvements included both digitized sounds and music samples.

Capcom's first mega-hit came with "Final Fight" in 1989. Up to that point in time, the "beat 'em up" genre had been dominated by Technos thanks to its excellent series of Kunio-kun (known outside of Japan as "Renegade") and the mega-hit Double Dragon.

With Cody, Guy, and Mike, Capcom cleared the room. Despite a minuscule budget of 2MiB for the graphics, the art team, led by Akira Yasuda (a.k.a Akiman) used the full capability of the CPS-1 to provide gorgeous visuals and engaging music. The gameplay was fantastic with various enemies, bosses, and skill-specific heroes. More importantly, the timing was right for the US market where "beat 'em up" was all the rage.

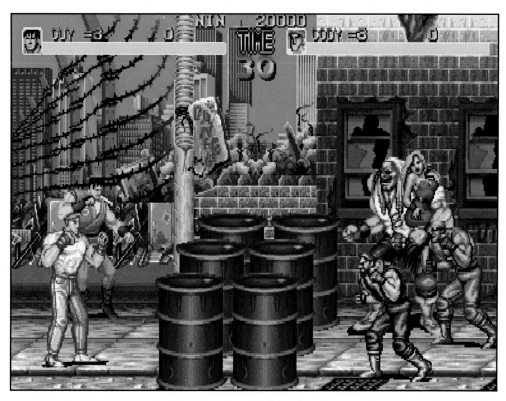

Final Fight (1989)

"Final Fight" soon became Capcom's top-selling game[8] and established the company as an undisputable arcade powerhouse.

Perhaps the best compliment came from competitors who, years later, would admit to the demoralizing effect "Final Fight" had on them.

> The people from Capcom hurt Technos Japan a lot with Final Fight which was superior on every level to Double Dragon III. Not only did they have amazing designers, they also gave their teams means to innovate thanks to the CPS-1.
>
> For us it was a horrible awakening because it proved we had been unable to evolve as fast as them.
>
> — Yoshihisa Kishimoto, Planner (Double Dragon & Kunio-kun planner) [10]

Not only was quality improved, quantity also increased. Thanks to its stable platform and tools, Capcom was able to release more than thirty titles between 1988 and 1995, all based on its CPS-1 platform.

Among them was the "Street Fighter" sequel which took the world by storm.

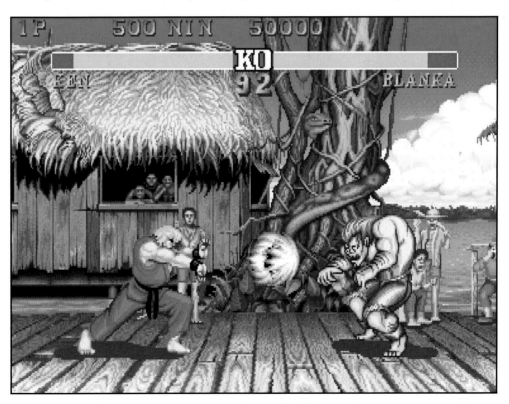

Street Fighter 2 (1991)

Game Name	Type			GFX	Year
Forgotten Worlds		☐		4 MiB	1988
Ghouls'n Ghosts		◼		3 MiB	1988
Strider		◼		4 MiB	1989
Dynasty Wars			◼	8 MiB	1989
Willow		◼		4 MiB	1989
U.N Squadron		☐		2 MiB	1989
Final Fight			◼	2 MiB	1989
1941: Counter Attack		☐		2 MiB	1990
Mercs	◼			3 MiB	1990
Mega Twins		◼		2 MiB	1990
Magic Sword		◼		2 MiB	1990
Carrier Air Wing		☐		2 MiB	1990
Nemo		◼		2 MiB	1990
Street Fighter II: The World Warrior			◼	6 MiB	1991
Three Wonders	◼			4 MiB	1991
The King of Dragons			◼	4 MiB	1991
Captain Commando			◼	4 MiB	1991
Knights of the Round			◼	4 MiB	1991
Street Fighter II: Champion Edition			◼	6 MiB	1992
Adventure Quiz: Capcom World 2	◼			2 MiB	1992
Varth: Operation Thunderstorm		☐		2 MiB	1992
Quiz & Dragons: Capcom Quiz Game	◼			2 MiB	1992
Street Fighter II' Turbo: Hyper Fighting			◼	6 MiB	1992
Ken Sei Mogura: Street Fighter II	◼			6 MiB	1993
Pnickies	◼			2 MiB	1993
Quiz Tonosama no Yabo 2	◼			4 MiB	1995
Pang! 3		◼		2 MiB	1995
Mega Man the Power Battle			◼	8 MiB	1995

CPS-1 games: ◼ Other, ◼ Platform, ☐ Shmup, ◼ Brawl, ◼ Duel

Sitting at the intersection of Capcom's new found technology and the "more-with-less" skills its teams had acquired out of necessity, "Street Fighter 2" was a quantum leap in gaming that resulted in a phenomenon.

The eight characters came in different sizes, shapes and genders. They each had their own moves and special abilities. These characterizations gave them depth. The music was engaging, and the sounds effects crisp. The precision of the controls invited players to build up their skills and master their avatar.

The hardware was capable of breathtaking per-line parallax running at a consistent, butter-smooth, 60Hz to showcase the artistic team's talent.

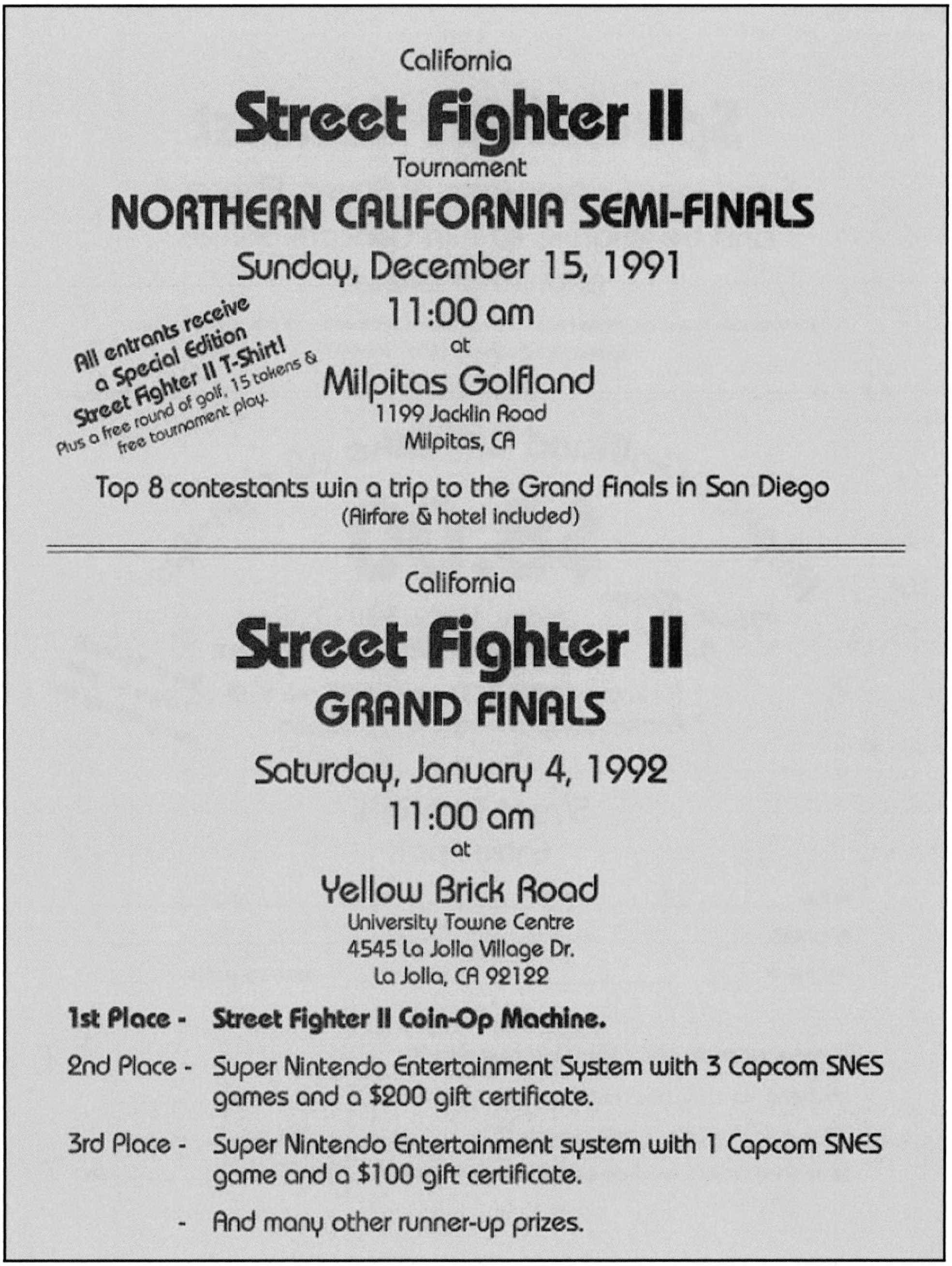

California

Street Fighter II

Tournament

NORTHERN CALIFORNIA SEMI-FINALS

Sunday, December 15, 1991

11:00 am

at

Milpitas Golfland

1199 Jacklin Road
Milpitas, CA

All entrants receive a Special Edition Street Fighter II T-Shirt! Plus a free round of golf, 15 tokens & free tournament play.

Top 8 contestants win a trip to the Grand Finals in San Diego
(Airfare & hotel included)

California

Street Fighter II

GRAND FINALS

Saturday, January 4, 1992

11:00 am

at

Yellow Brick Road

University Towne Centre
4545 La Jolla Village Dr.
La Jolla, CA 92122

1st Place - **Street Fighter II Coin-Op Machine.**

2nd Place - Super Nintendo Entertainment System with 3 Capcom SNES games and a $200 gift certificate.

3rd Place - Super Nintendo Entertainment system with 1 Capcom SNES game and a $100 gift certificate.

- And many other runner-up prizes.

Street Fighter 2 tournament flyer

The game immediately developed a cult following. Players had to wait in lines to drop a quarter. Purchasing "Continue" was frowned upon by other players impatiently waiting for their turns. Operators purchased multiple copies of the game to reduce wait times, and at the end of the day machines still overflowed with coins[45].

The popularity was such that tournaments with handsome rewards (opposing page) were held.

By 1995, the series had generated $2.3 billion with 200,000 cabinets sold[12] (60,000 World Warriors units and 140,000 Champion Edition units). By 2017 that figure reached $10.61 billion[13], making "Street Fighter 2" the third top grossing game of all time.

> **Trivia:** Did you notice this ubiquitous player nicknamed **NiN** who owns all the high-scores of Forgotten Worlds (p27), Final Fight (p29), and Street Fighter II (p30)? It is the pseudonym of Akira Nishitani, the gameplay planner on all these titles!

1.4 Ode to CP-System

This book is an engineering love letter to the system that enabled Capcom to evolve from a company fighting for survival to become an arcade household name.

The goal of this work is to understand the CP-System, from the ground up. This will (hopefully) be achieved by first exposing the hardware and then progressively moving up, all the way to the programming and game engine architecture level.

Hardware

The CP-System is comprised of four hardware subsystems which are explored in the first chapter.

- Control System
- Audio System
- GFX System
- Video System

Beyond the hard reality of silicon and bus lines, a discussion of the design choices and real-life examples of how games leveraged features is provided when relevant.

Software

The subsequent chapters study the software and how to build it. In particular the four ROM groups that make up a game are explained.

- Motorola m68k ROM

- Zilog z80 programming and YM2151 (music) ROM

- MSM6295 (audio samples) ROM

- CPS-A/CPS-B (GFX) ROM

These chapters use modern tooling but also feature a "Back in the days" section which explores how Capcom used to work back in the '90s.

Peopleware

People involved with either hardware or software are quoted in the relevant sections. However, Capcom was already a big company by the early '90s and many ended up participating in the history of the CPS-1. To help the reader keep track of all the actors, a list of people and their roles is available on page 225.

Hardware

The project that would later be dubbed by the press "superchip"[25] started between 1985 and 1986. It was a massive investment that would require two years and five million dollars[5] (the equivalent of $12 million in 2022).

The significant time and funds invested left no ambiguity in the mind of Capcom executives. This project would dictate the life or death of the company.

> The CP-System is an extremely important business strategy to Capcom: we have gambled everything on it.
>
> — Yoshiki Okamoto, Capcom Producer[26]

2.1 Goals

The CPS-1 was expected to solve most of Capcom's arcade division problems. Namely: reduce production cost, lower selling price, streamline development, increase GFX/SFX/processing capabilities, and stop piracy.

Cost reduction would be achieved by mimicking home consoles and standardizing the platform. Instead of re-designing boards for each game, the hardware would be a constant with the cabinet differentiated only by the software running on it.

Price lowering would allow arcade operators to replace their games more often. This objective would be reached by designing a platform where new game boards containing mostly ROMs could be purchased separately from the processor board.

The development toolchain would improve thanks to the stability of the target platform. Without having to constantly rewrite tools and juggle with assembly languages, programmers could invest in the long term and build an SDK running on powerful workstations such as SHARP's series of X68000s.

Most importantly, games had to catch customer eyes and not pale in comparison to the competition. The goal was to design a machine with capabilities an order of magnitude above the current tech stack, able to generate audio and visuals that held their own compared to titles from powerhouses such as Sega or Namco.

Finally was the problem of piracy. In a country like Mexico it was estimated that 200,000 PCB bootlegs were in circulation[45] despite Capcom recording no sales in that territory. Multiple concurrent copy-protection mechanisms needed to be implemented.

2.2   JAMMA

Arcade operators frequently updated their cabinets by replacing the game it ran in order to keep bringing novelty to players and quarters to their pockets. Thanks to the **J**apan **A**musement **M**achine and **M**arketing **A**ssociation, the process of updating was simple.

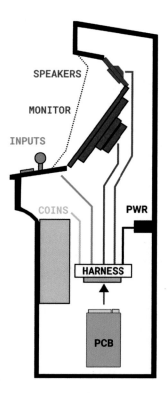

The belly of these machines usually hid an abomination of tangled wires converging in a JAMMA harness where the motherboard would be inserted as a slot-in. All an operator had to do was swap the old with the new PCBs.

A JAMMA port has everything a game needs to operate. Its 28 pins on each side provide inputs (four-direction joystick and three buttons per player, two coin sensors, start button, and service button), outputs (mono speakers lines and "monitor" controls), and even power supply.

The problem with such a standard is that while it improves interoperability, it also hinders innovation.

A few pins on the port are not reserved for a specific usage but they could not be used for extra features since once the harness was wired, operators did not want to touch it.

JAMMA CHIPS / TOP		
1	GND	
2	GND	
3	+5V	
4	+5V	
5	-5V	
6	+12V	
8	COIN #1	
9	LOCK COIL1	
10	SPEAKER +	
12	VIDEO R	
13	VIDEO B	
14	VIDEO GND	
16	COIN #1	
17	P1 START	
18	P1 UP	
19	P1 DOWN	
20	P1 LEFT	
21	P1 RIGHT	
22	P1 KEY #1	
23	P1 KEY #2	
24	P1 KEY #3	
25	EXTRA	
26	EXTRA	
27	GND	
28	GND	

JAMMA parts side pins

JAMMA SOLDER/BOTTOM		
A	GND	
B	GND	
C	+5V	
D	+5V	
E	-5V	
F	+12V	
J	SPEAKER -	
L	VIDEO G	
M	VIDEO SYNC	
N		
P		
R	COIN #2	
S	P2 START	
T	P2 UP	
U	P2 DOWN	
V	P2 LEFT	
W	P2 RIGHT	
X	P2 KEY #1	
Y	P2 KEY #2	
Z	P2 KEY #3	
a	EXTRA	
b	EXTRA	
c		
d		
e	GND	
f	GND	

JAMMA bottom side pins

When Capcom retrofitted Street Fighter 1 pneumatic buttons, they chose to do it with six buttons per player, which was three more than available in JAMMA. To circumvent the limitation, they designed a parallel input system.

Since the three JAMMA buttons were used for punches, the extension was labeled the "kick harness".

Wire Color	Pin #	Function
Black	1	GND
Black	2	GND
Purple	3	Player 1 Light Kick
Grey	4	Player 1 Medium Kick
White	5	Player 1 Heavy Kick
	6	NC
Orange	7	Player 2 Light Kick
Green	8	Player 2 Medium Kick
Blue	9	Player 2 Heavy Kick
	10	NC

Kick harness pinouts

37

2.3 Physical Architecture

The CP-System is made of three printed circuit boards named Board "A", Board "B", and Board "C" which are stacked on top of each other.

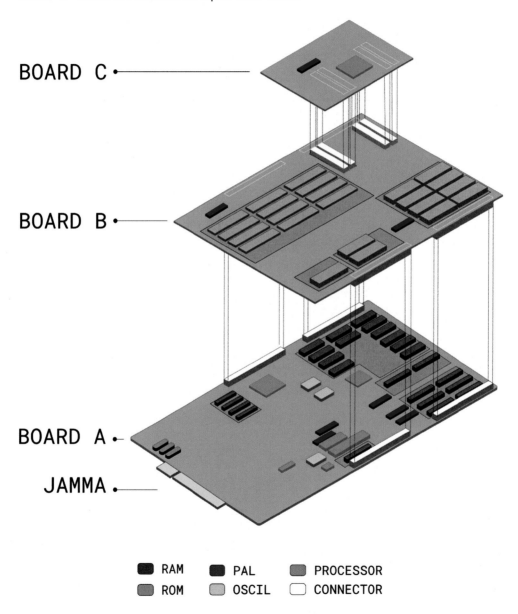

The connection points are prominent white connectors. Boards A and B are connected via four 2x32-pin connectors while the boards B and C are connected with four 2x20-pin connectors. Once plugged into each other, the boards are manipulated as a whole with no floating parts.

The system was revised over the years. Approximately 229 variations are known to exist, including bootlegs[15]. The board which will be studied in this book is the one used to run "Street Fighter 2": board A "88617A-7B", board B "90629B", and board C "90628-C".

2.3.1 Board A

Board "A" is the platform that never changes between games. It features all but one of the chips in charge of processing data, whether it is game logic, audio, or video.

A summary look at page 40 reveals the powerhouse of the whole system. Even an untrained eye will notice the size of the **A**pplication-**S**pecific **I**ntegrated **C**ircuit (ASIC) and the sheer number of bus lines leading to it. In the center left stands the "CPS-A", in charge of 50% of the graphic system and its 16MHz oscillator. Just above is 384 KiB of VRAM to store a special kind of framebuffer studied in later pages.

Directly below the CPS-A is the video system and its 8 KiB of SRAM containing the palettes.

The upper right section is the control system with a Motorola m68k, a 10MHz oscillator, 64 KiB of "work" SRAM and 192KiB of GFX SRAM.

The middle right part is where the audio system lives. It is made of a Zilog z80, a 3.58MHz oscillator, and 2 KiB of "work" SRAM. Also in this area are the audio chips dedicated to music (YM2151 and YM3012) and sound effects (OKI6295).

Finally, in the bottom part we find all the components taking care of the inputs and outputs of the JAMMA connector. Alongside are three DIP switches which an arcade operator can use to configure game parameters such as game difficulty or how many credits a coin grants.

There are many chips on these three boards but it would be a mistake to conclude that combining many processors inevitably leads to better performance. That would be ignoring issues such as bus congestion, bus size difference, bus timings or even processor endianness.

To design an effective multi-CPUs system able to avoid both instruction and data starvation is in fact far from trivial.

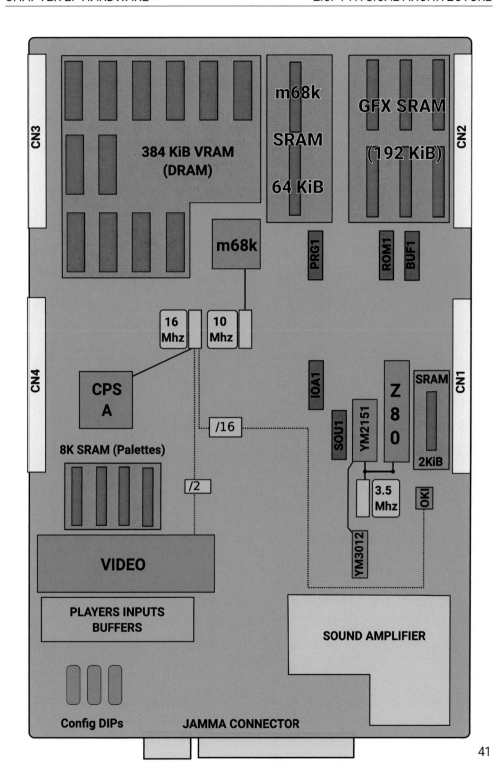

2.3.2 Board B

Board B is where the ROM chips containing all the assets and instructions specific to a game are attached via DIP sockets. The chips are not soldered but push-in mounted (and easily removable).

Even though all ROM chips are located on the same board, they are not all part of an unified data system on an unified bus.

ROM chips are grouped depending on the system they belong to. Each group has its own data lines connected to a dedicated bus leading to a specific processor.

Thirty-eight DIP slots are visible on the board. They are grouped in four ROM groups.

Empty board B

There are 3x8 = 24 chips, referred to as "GFX ROM", dedicated to storing GFX via sockets [1-8], sockets [10-17], and sockets [20-27] for a total of 12 MiB capacity. Because of the price of ROM, games were never budgeted to allow the max capacity. Most titles were granted 2/4MiB, three (the Street Fighter II series) were allowed 6 MiB, and one (Dynasty Wars) got a whopping 8 MiB.

One socket (9) with 64KiB capacity, referred as "z80 ROM", stores both the z80 instructions and the music assets (instructions for the YM2151).

Two sockets (18-19) accounting for 256 KiB, referred as "OKI ROM", store ADPCM samples and are directly connected to the OKI chip.

Finally eight ROMs holding 1 MiB, referred as "M68K ROM", are dedicated to hosting m68k instructions. Even though they are related to graphics, palettes are also stored in this ROM group.

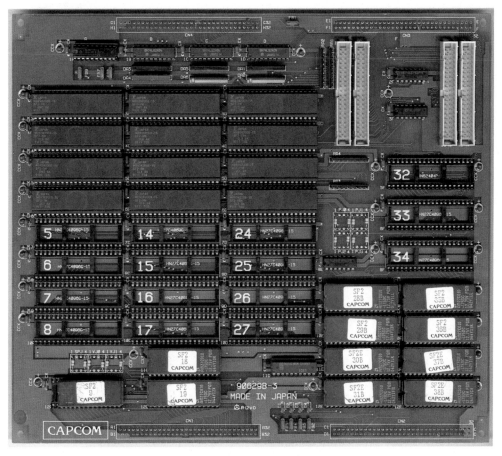

Board B with Street Fighter 2 ROMs

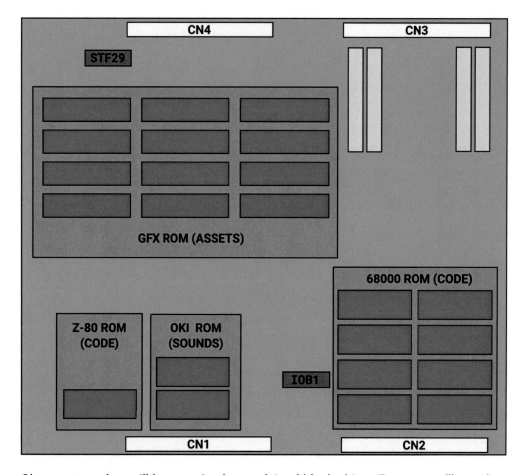

Observant readers will have noticed unexplained black chips. For now we'll say they are in charge of bus traffic management. In the drawing above, `STF29` handles the GFX ROM and `IOB1` handles the m68k ROM. As an exercise, go back to page 41 and guess which chip handles which ROM/RAM group. Or don't, I am just a book.

2.3.3 Board C

Board "C" hosts the "CPS-B" ASIC video chip. It is in charge of the remaining 50% of the graphic pipeline, namely mixing data from the VRAM and the GFX ROMs towards the pixel generator. Capcom also concentrated its anti-piracy measures in this chip and as a result revised board "C" many more times than board A and board B.

This will be discussed extensively in the copy-protection section of this chapter.

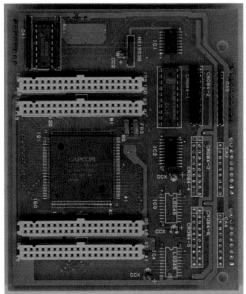 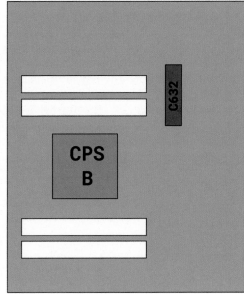

2.3.4 PALs

The black chips on the drawing are called **P**rogrammable **A**rray **L**ogic (PAL). They play a crucial role in the creation of the memory maps.

They pack boolean logic (&, |, !) between their input and output lines which simplifies the board, allows tuning the logic without changing the PCB hardware lines, and reduces the number of components.

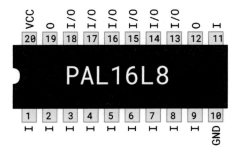

Often located near the memory chip group they affect, they are codenamed based on their function. Since most games use slightly different ROM layout, they usually feature different PALs, e.g: the chip which organizes the GFX ROM is named STF29 in Street Fighter II, S224B in Final Fight, and DM620 in Ghouls'n Ghosts.

2.4   Logical Architecture

The CP-System features eight processors, organized hierarchically. Commands issued at the top are carried out to sub-systems via a chain of reports.

There is strong isolation via layering where top systems are unable to access sub-systems resources. e.g: Control has no access to VRAM and audio ROM.

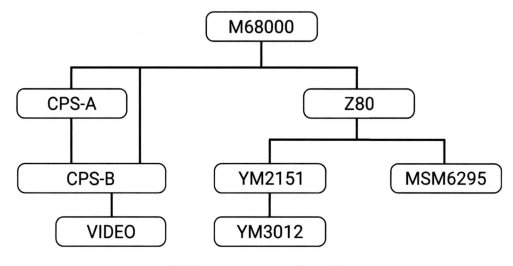

CP-System processor hierarchy

The control system features a m68k in charge of coordinating inputs (joystick, buttons, coin) and outputs (video and audio). It can communicate with both the GFX and audio system main processors.

The audio system runs almost totally in isolation. It is connected to control via two 8-bit latches which the z80 actively polls to retrieve commands related to music and sound effects. Notice how these latches bridge different data bus widths since control has 16 data lines while the audio system uses 8 data lines.

The graphic system needs more communications and exposes not only its CPS-A and CPS-B registers but also the GFX RAM where the screen layout is described. The m68k and the CPS-A use the same bus to access the GFX RAM, so the demarcation is not as clean as with the audio system. This results in a bit of bus contention.

The video system produces a stream of palette addresses. Combined with the palette SRAM (where colors are stored) and the DAC, it outputs a signal towards JAMMA. It is heavy duty in order to keep up with the 59.64Hz refresh rate desired on the screen.

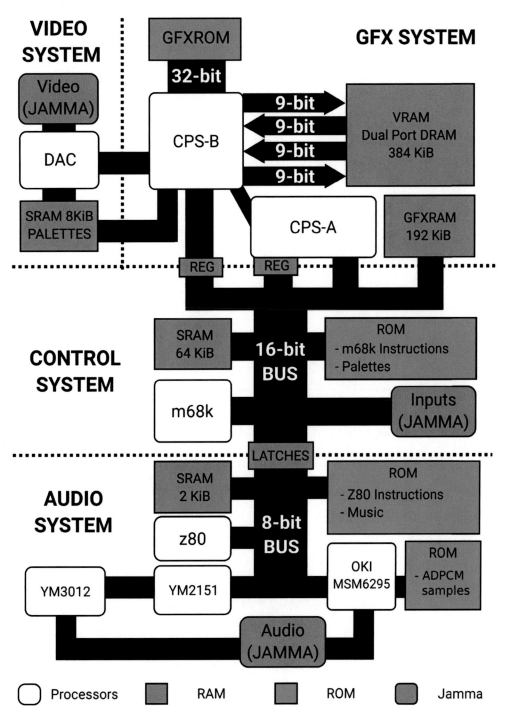

CPS-1 logical architecture with data lines

2.5   Control System

The control system oversees the platform. As a ruler it needs not to excel at a specific task but to be able to direct and keep tabs on many components. This is a task tailor-made for the Motorola 68000.

2.5.1   Motorola 68000 CPU

Released in 1979 and clocked at 10 MHz (later upgraded to 12 MHz), the 68000 with its two stage pipeline[35] (prefetch, exec) and no internal cache was not a particularly powerful chip by late 80s standards. Its 1.7 MIPS placed it on par with an Intel 286 10MHz (1.5 MIPS). By 1989 it was already two generations old behind the 1984 M68020 (3 MIPS) and the 1987 M68030 (5 MIPS)[9].

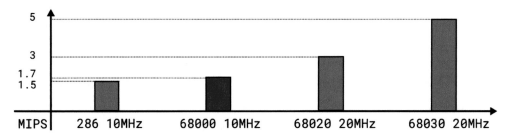

However, this lack of speed did not prevent a plethora of manufacturers from using it as their backbone. On the list of machines adopting the m68k can be found the Atari ST, Amiga, Sega's System 16, Genesis, Sega CD, Apple Macintosh, Sharp X68000, and even SNK's Neo-Geo. It was even IBM's first choice for its PC before production issues allowed the Intel 8088 to prevail[34].

Performance is not what made the 68000 reign as the prime hardware design choice. The reason this CPU was so successful is because it was a great team player.

While most machines used a 16-bit address system, its 24-bit address space allowed the 68000 16 MiB of RAM, which was considered humongous at the time. This was a considerable advantage when it came to map peripherals. There was so much address space that, had they wished so, Capcom engineers could have allowed the 68000 to see all RAM and all ROM of all systems on the CPS-1.

While other CPUs used small address registers resulting in the infamous segmented addressing, Motorola gave its CPU 32-bit data and address registers. The elegant flat addressing and generous eighteen registers made it a favorite among programmers.

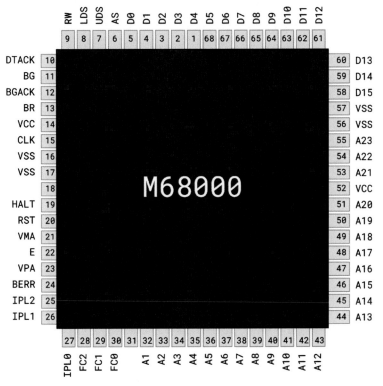

Motorola 68000 pin-outs

The 68000 is brought to life via its clock (CLK), +5V (VCC), and Ground (VSS) pins.

The bus is made of D0-D7 for data and A0-A15 for addresses while address ACK (AS), Read/Write (R/W), UDS , LDS , and Data ACK DTACK are bus control pins.

Arbitration to allow peripherals to master the bus is done with Bus Request (BR), Bus Grant (BG) and Bus Grant ACK (GBA-K) lines.

The interrupt system is made of a generous three pins IPL0 , IPL1 , IPL2 , and VPA for control. While other CPUs like the x86s or the z80 have a single interrupt line, the multiple IPL s can encode an interrupt ID directly which removes the need for an interrupt controller. How this is leveraged will be explained in the programming section.

System control is done via Bus Error (BERR), Reset (RST), and Halt (HALT).

Finally, the processor status is given by FC0 , FC1 , FC2 and Peripheral control is done via sync (E) and valid sig (VMA).

Trivia: Motorola's CPU name is due to the total number of transistors totaling 68,000 units. The 68030 and 68040 had more transistors than their names indicate.

Despite the raving description provided in the previous pages, the 68000 could be a peculiar CPU to program. Its most famous shortcoming involved memory alignment. While Intel's line of CISC allows random memory accesses (at the cost of a great performance penalty), Motorola's CPU will throw an `address error` exception while attempting to read/write memory not aligned on a 16-bit (`WORD`) boundary.

This limitation is rooted all the way down to the CPU pins where there is no `A0` line. Pins `UDS` and `LDS` indicate which of the high-byte or low-byte parts of a 16-bit `WORD` to access.

Trivia: The 68000 has 32-bit address registers but used only 24-bit addresses. These "unused" eight bits were hijacked by system engineers to mark address as "locked" or "purgeable". These programs promptly broke when running on a 68020, which used a 32-bit address bus.

Perhaps the best testament to the quality of the 68000 design is that as of 2022, 43 years after its release, Motorola's immortal CPU is still in production.

2.5.2   Motorola 68000 "work" RAM

With 16-bit data bus processors it would be fair to expect a memory system built with 16-bit RAM chips. However these were expensive and a closer look reveals a bunch of `65256BLSP-10` offering fast access time (100ns SRAM) and 32 KiB capacity but only 8 data lines.

Using cheaper off-the-shelf 8-bit RAM chips instead of 16-bit RAM chips helped to drive down cost. Moreover, these are not hard to combine into a 16-bit RAM system via two-way interleave.

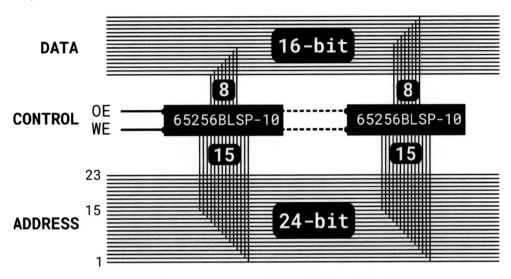

32 Ki x 16-bit RAM system with two 32 Ki x 8-bit chips

The two `65256BLSP-10` are not aware of each other. They are connected to the same 15 address lines and the same control lines for Write Enabled (`WE`) and Read Enabled (`OE`). However, they are connected to different lines of the data bus.

> **Trivia:** Interleaving chips can also help to beat memory latency by increasing throughput. Early GPUs such as the Voodoo 1 and Voodoo 2 by 3Dfx extensively relied on this technique, even using four-way interleave to keep up with the bandwidth requirements[6].

Notice how the address lines of the SRAM chips are directly connected to the 68000 address bus. There is no mechanism to prevent these two chips from responding to all bus requests.

This is an over-simplification to introduce complexity progressively. We will see next how chips are organized to not conflict with each other.

> **Trivia:** 64 KiB of work RAM seems like a lot but was not always enough. Some games found themselves with not enough RAM and too much GFXRAM. Street Fighter 2 Champion Edition programmers resolved to generating and executing instructions from the GFXRAM[16]!

2.5.3   Motorola 68000 Program ROM

The 68000 instructions are provided by eight `27C010` which are 128 Ki x 8-bit chips. They work like the `65256BLSP-10` except that they have sixteen address lines instead of fifteen (and therefore higher capacity).

Like the RAM, ROM chips are combined via two-way interleaves to provide 16-bit data. What is peculiar is how the four pairs are arranged to build a memory system with larger capacity.

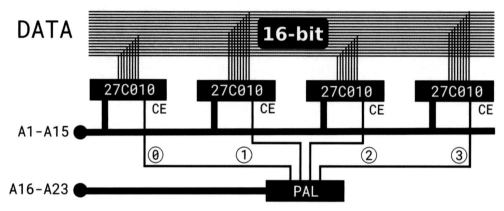

Two first pairs. 4 x (128 Ki x 8-bit) making a 256Ki x 16-bit system

To place one pair after another in memory space, the `CE` (Chip Enabled, sometimes labeled `CS` for "Chip Selected") pin is leveraged. Asserting it lets a chip respond to an address request while de-asserting it keeps it dormant. All CEs on all chips on all boards are controlled via PALs.

In this example, the first four out PAL pins must be programmed as follows.

```
Output 0 = !(A16  |   A17 | A18 | A19 | A20 | A21 | A22 | A23)
Output 1 = !(A16  |   A17 | A18 | A19 | A20 | A21 | A22 | A23)
Output 2 =   A16 &! (A17 | A18 | A19 | A20 | A21 | A22 | A23)
Output 3 =   A16 &! (A17 | A18 | A19 | A20 | A21 | A22 | A23)
```

The first pair of chips is mapped to addresses `0x000000` while the second pair is mapped to `0x40000`. With the same logic, two more pairs of `27C010` are mapped at `0x80000` and `0xc0000` for a total of 1 MiB ROM.

By now, it should be abundantly clear that the `CE` / `CS` lines are absolutely crucial to build a memory map. Even though they won't be mentioned again, keep in mind they impact every chip on the boards (except the CPUs).

2.5.4   68000 Memory Map

Thanks to the PAL chips enabling/disabling components, the 68000's memory space is partitioned. The result is summarized in a "memory map".

Start	End	Size	Function
0x000000	0x3FFFFF	4 MiB	ROM
0x800000	0x800007	8 B	JAMMA Players Inputs
0x800018	0x80001F	8 B	JAMMA Dip Switches
0x800030	0x800037	8 B	JAMMA Coin sensors
0x800176	0x800177	2 B	Kick harness
0x800100	0x80013f	64 B	CPS-A registers
0x800140	0x80017f	64 B	CPS-B registers
0x800180	0x800187	8 B	Sound commands (latch 1)
0x800188	0x80018F	8 B	Sound commands (latch 2)
0x900000	0x92FFFF	192 KiB	GFXRAM
0xFF0000	0xFFFFFF	64 KiB	Work RAM

Control system memory map

2.5.5   Putting it All Together

The details of the 68000's operations will be studied in-depth in the next chapters but we can already guess how the CPU operates based on what it can access. As the m68k boots, it starts to retrieve instructions from its ROM. For regular operations such as store/load, and also to keep track of its call stack, it uses its work RAM.

The game engine starts and reads the configuration set by the arcade operators via the DIP switches. While the game runs, the CPU continuously polls the JAMMA inputs.

The engine reads JAMMA inputs and delegates generation of video and audio signal to its subordinates. In turn these generate signals towards JAMMA outputs.

For the video, the m68k describes the scene to be displayed via the GFXRAM. The graphic ASICs are then instructed how to retrieve the scene data via their registers.

For the audio, the m68k issues simple commands to the z80 via two 1 byte latches using a protocol detailed later.

2.6   Audio System

The audio system runs in isolation from everything else. It has its own bus, its own RAM, its own ROM systems, and its own oscillators. Its only opening to the outside world are two latches to receive commands from the control system and two JAMMA pins to output sound.

The component in charge is a surprisingly lightweight z80 running at 3.58 MHz.

2.6.1   z80 CPU

Released in July 1976 by Zilog, the z80 was intended as an Intel 8080 killer thanks to a compatible instruction set. It ended up becoming an icon of the 70s, sharing the scene with the equally legendary MOS 6502 well into the mid-80s.

The z80 was widely used in home computers, notably featured in the Sinclair ZX Spectrum and the Amstrad CPC. It also found its way into military applications, musical equipment (Roland Jupiter-8), embedded systems, and multiple coin-op arcades.

As an 8-bit era processor, the z80 uses 8-bit data registers, 8-bit data bus, 16-bit addresses, and 16-bit address bus. In terms of processing power, despite its "overlapping fetch/execute" design the CPU had become particularly weak by late 80s standards with 0.45 MIPS. It was three times slower than the 68000 featured in the control system[9].

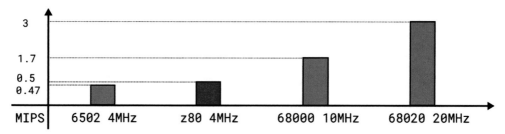

Processing power was not the deciding factor in electing the master of the Sound system, though. Thanks to its two powerful co-processors, the CPU would not have to process much data, making the MIPS figure irrelevant. A much more important characteristic was how well it integrated with its two sidekicks.

Thanks to its 8-bit design, the z80 was a perfect fit for the 8-bit YM2151 and the 8-bit MSM6295. Having been around for a while, the "outdated" CPU was inexpensive. Lastly, it enjoyed a good reputation thanks to its simple programming interface.

> **Trivia:** The number of pin lines on a chip dictates its packaging name. DIP (Dual In-line Package), like the z80 below, are recognizable by their two lines of pins. The Motorola 68000 on page 49 with its four sides of pins belongs to the "Chip carrier" family.
>
> Packaging can use materials such as plastic or ceramic in which cases they are referred to by increasingly barbaric acronyms such as CLCC or PLCC.

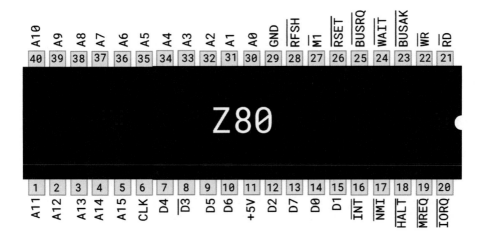

The z80 comes to life thanks to its `CLK` (clock), `+5V` (power), and `GND` (ground) pins.

The bus lines are dedicated `A0-A15` for addresses and `D0-D7` for data. For control, `RD` indicates read while `WR` indicates a write operation. `WAIT` is used to add waitstates.

Although it is capable of relinquishing control of the bus via `BUSRQ` (Bus Request), `BUSAK` (Bus Acknowledge), `MREQ` (Memory Request), and `IORQ` (IO Request), the z80 completely owns its bus and never shares it. In fact, the `BUSRQ` and `BUSAK` pins are not even connected. Because it is isolated via latches, the z80's bus never suffers contention.

Other pins are `NMI` Non Maskable Interrupt, `RESET` Restart CPU, `HALT` Waiting for interrupt, `M1` Fetching next instruction. The `INT` Interrupt line will be of crucial interest in the programming section. An interrupt controller is usually necessary but the simple needs of the sound system allows it to work without one.

The `RFSH` pin (ReFreSH signal) ticks at regular intervals to trigger DRAM refreshes. Since the sound system uses only SRAM this pin was re-purposed in a creative way for the CPS-1.5 "Kabuki" (page 124).

2.6.2   z80 Work RAM

The amount of RAM provided to the z80 may appear scandalously small by today's standards. However because all it has to do is forward requests from the latches to the MSM6295 and feed the YM2151 music notes, the z80 needs few resources. Its bus is connected to a single 2Ki x 8-bit `CXK5816SP` chip.

2.6.3   z80 ROM

The ROM is made of a simple 64Ki x 8-bit `27C512` chip. It is much larger than the RAM in order to store YM2151 instructions alongside the z80 instructions.

These ROM chips work like those previously described, with pins such as power, ground, addresses, data, control, and of course the crucial `CE`. What is peculiar is the z80 uses 16-bit address registers which allows 65,536 addresses. There is not enough address space for all registers, ROM, and RAM totaling 67 KiB.

The solution is to map only the portion of the ROM that contains instructions (32KiB) statically and to use a banking system to provide a 16 KiB "view" into the remaining 32KiB of the ROM where music assets are stored. This is accomplished simply with a PAL (`SOU1`) and was a source of great pain to the developers (see page 138).

Hopefully the thought of this awful bank switch control register will leave no doubt with regards to the awesomeness of the m68k and its 24-bit flat addressing system.

2.6.4   z80 Memory Map

Start	End	Size	Function
0x0000	0x7FFF	32 KiB	ROM (32 KiB out of 64 KiB)
0x8000	0xBFFF	16 KiB	Bank-switched view of rest of ROM
0xD000	0xD7FF	2 KiB	RAM
0xF000	0xF001	2 B	YM2151 registers
0xF002	0xF002	1 B	OKI OKI6295 registers
0xF004	0xF004	1 B	Bank Switch control (`SOU1`)
0xF006	0xF006	1 B	OKI MSM6295 H / L mode
0xF008	0xF008	1 B	Sound commands (latch 1)
0xF00A	0xF00A	1 B	Sound commands (latch 2)

Audio memory map

2.6.5   YM2151

Selecting the music chip was not a matter of shopping between vendors but rather picking one from Yamaha. Thanks to the licensing of Frequency Modulation (FM) patents from Stanford in 1975, the Japanese founder ruled the world of electronic music.

> **Trivia:** Yamaha licensed FM technology from Stanford starting in 1975 at the cost of $10/keyboard. Licensing was renegotiated in 1985 on a per-chip basis[7].

Three architectures stood out in the early 90s. Between the OPL2 3812, the OPN2 2612, and the OPM (**OP**erator type **M**) 2151, the latter was selected for its versatility.

The principle of Frequency Modulation is to use simple wave forms to modulate each other in a Modulator/Carrier pair, resulting in complex waveforms[41].

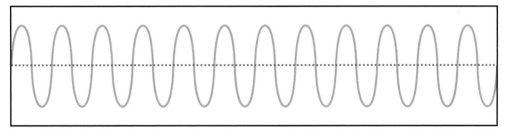

Carrier wave

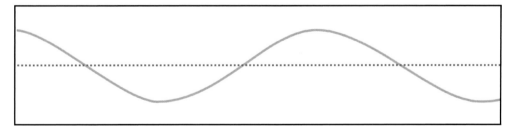

Modulator wave

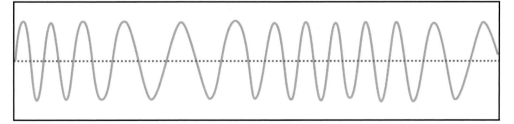

Resulting wave

The YM2151 is able to play 8 channels (a.k.a voices) of audio. Each channel consists of four operators (a.k.a slots) which can be setup to produce either percussion or instrument sounds.

Slots are even able to modulate their own output. With proper adjustments, virtually any wave form can be obtained.

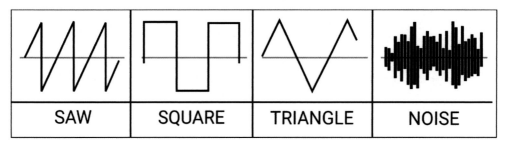

Some of the wave forms the YM2151 can generate

Other parameters can be applied to a channel's output. The envelope features adjustable Attack, Decay, Sustain, and Release Rate.

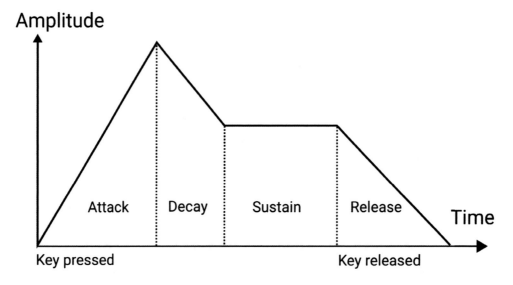

The huge advantage of FM synthesis is the small amount of data required to store a melody. After the instruments are defined, only the notes of each instrument and their tempo need to be recorded. Yamaha's technology is so efficient that in Street Fighter 2 the whole Sagat main stage music (2mn6s, 10KiB) uses fewer bytes than one Tiger Uppercut's ADPCM sample (777ms, 12KiB).

Looking at the YM2151, we see previously discussed pins such as +5V, GND, and CS. The CLK is connected to the same oscillator as the z80 for a frequency of 3.58MHz. The D0–D7 address/data pins (multiplexed via A0) exactly fit the z80's 8-bit data bus with read (RD) and write (WR) control.

One pin is of particular interest to us. IRQ allows the YM2151 to generate interrupts based on two internal counters. Its usage is detailed in the programming section.

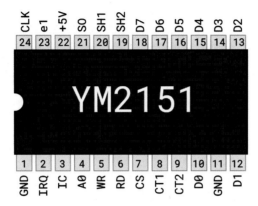

The only drawback of this chip is that it does not feature a DAC (Digital to Analog Converter). It generates a signal on the Serial Output (SO).

2.6.6 YM3012

The YM3012 is a DAC connected to the YM2151 digital output SO. The analog signal it outputs on CH1 and CH2 is mixed with the signal from the OKI6295 towards JAMMA.

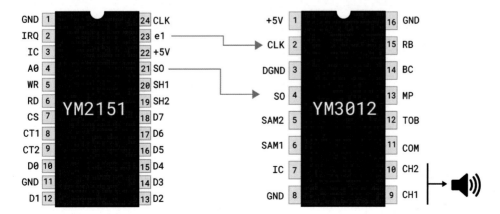

2.6.7   MSM6295

For audio sample playback, Capcom spared no expense and selected a chip capable of 4-bit ADPCM audio decompression over four channels, the MSM6295 (a.k.a OKI).

Despite running at only 1MHz, the MSM6295 is a god-send to a game board designer. It does not need instructions as its function is fully hard-coded. Its address (A0–A15) and data (D0–D7) lines are directly connected to its own 256 KiB ROM, on a local bus where assets are stored. This avoids contention with the z80 bus.

These make it a fully enclosed digitized sound system only communicated via its input lines (I0–I7), a perfect match for the z80 data bus, from which it receives commands.

To get to work, the OKI only needs to receive a sample ID [1-127], a channel [1-4], and a volume [0-127]. Via a lookup table in its ROM, the sample offset is retrieved and playback starts with an analog signal generated on DA0 .

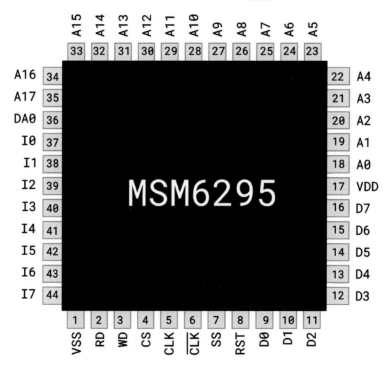

Up to four channels can be active simultaneously. Since games don't need that many sound effects simultaneously, two channels are usually reserved for sound effect playback while two are dedicated to embellishing music with samples.

ADPCM lossy compression is able to divide space consumption by three by converting 12-bit PCM samples into 4-bit nibbles.

Making choices

While the choice of the Yamaha music chip left little ambiguity to the hardware designer, the MSM6295 was a different story.

First, the sampling rate expected in ROM is directly correlated to the clock rate of the MSM6295. Second, the OKI can operate in two modes via its SS pin. In high quality (H), the divisor is 132 and in low quality (L) the divisor is 165.

Running within [1MHz-5MHz] in two modes, the goal was to maximize quality while minimizing required storage. The table below shows that the best quality (37kHz) only allowed storage of 13 seconds of samples, while the lowest quality (6060Hz) gave 86 seconds.

	H		L	
MHz	**Sampling Rate (Hz)**	**Time (s)**	**Sampling Rate (Hz)**	**Time (s)**
1	7575	69	6060	86
2	15151	34	12121	43
3	22727	23	18181	28
4	30303	17	24242	21
5	37878	13	30303	17

MSM6295 operating modes (with ROM = 256 KiB).

In the end, Capcom connected the OKI to the GFX crystal (16MHz) and divided frequency by 16 to run at 1MHz. Along with a SS pin set to H, the system uses a 7,575Hz sampling rate.

2.6.8   PCM 101

The MSM6295 input and output are respectively ADPCM and PCM streams. To deepen our understanding of the chip requires studying how **P**ulse-**C**ode **M**odulation works.

Whether for recording or playing, PCM is a series of values directly representing the position of a device diaphragm. In the case of recording, the diaphragm is in a microphone. In playing, it is in a loud speaker.

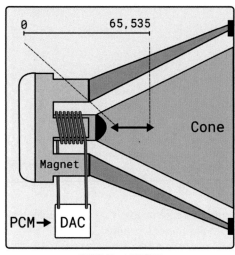 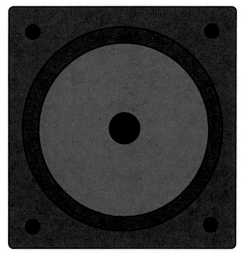

SIDE VIEW   FRONT VIEW

A speaker cone moves proportionally to the PCM values

Sampling rate and bit depth are the two parameters impacting the fidelity of the signal capture/restitution.

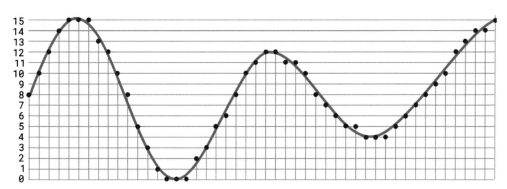

PCM values (4-bit samples) quantizing an analog signal

The higher the sampling rate (on the X axis), the more often the cone position can be adjusted. The higher the bit depth (on the Y axis), the more accurately the cone position can be set. Stereo is achieved by interleaving two PCM streams.

Sound quality increases linearly with data rate.

- Landline phones use 8,000Hz/8-bit mono using 8,000 Bytes per Second.

- CDs use 44,100Hz/16-bit stereo using 176,400 Bytes per Second.

2.6.9 ADPCM Compression

ADPCM is able to take 12-bit PCM samples and compress then as 4-bit nibbles by encoding only the difference between PCM samples. Decompressing an ADPCM stream consists of adding a delta value to the last decompressed sample, over and over again.

The delta is encoded with a system of weighted offsets called "step", which is accurate for small variations but coarser when deltas increase.

The first bit in a nibble indicates the sign of the delta (+/-). The three other give a "magnitude". The magnitude depends on the "step size" of the ADPCM decompressor.

ADPCM nibble

In its initial state, the step size is 16 which means bit three is +/-16, bit two +/-8 and bit one +/-4. In this state, the delta to be applied can vary from 0 (b000) to +/- 28 (b111).

The decompressor constantly monitors how much of the step size is used. The step size is adjusted after each sample via a predetermined transition table indexed via the magnitude value.

```
int stepSizes[49] = { // Indexed by stepSizeIndex
    16,   17,   19,   21,    23,    25,    28,
    31,   34,   37,   41,    45,    50,    55,
    60,   66,   73,   80,    88,    97,   107,
   118,  130,  143,  157,   173,   190,   209,
   230,  253,  279,  307,   337,   371,   408,
   449,  494,  544,  598,   658,   724,   796,
   876,  963, 1060, 1166,  1282,  1411,  1552};

int stepSizeIndex = 0; // Initial value (0) points to 16

//  indexed by MAG           0   1   2   3  4  5  6  7
int transitionTable[8] = {-1, -1, -1, -1, 2, 4, 6, 8};
```

The transition table dictates how to adjust the step size index. ADPCM is aggressive in increasing the index for magnitude values ranging from 4 to 7 where it is bumped between 2 and 8 . Meanwhile it is conservative in decreasing the index for small magnitude values ranging from 0 to 3 where it is always modified in -1 decrements.

2.7 Video System

The goal of the video system is to pilot the CRT (Cathode-Ray Tube) where images are rasterized for the player to see.

Even though it is connected via an intermediate JAMMA port, there is no abstraction layer or custom protocol. The four red, green, blue, and sync JAMMA output pins are connected directly into the CRT inputs.

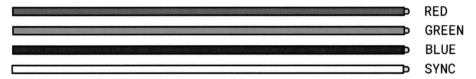

RED
GREEN
BLUE
SYNC

The four wires needed to drive a CRT

There are four wires but in fact five signals are transmitted. Each red, green, and blue signal has its own wire, while the sync wire carries two signals multiplexed as horizontal sync pulse and vertical sync pulse. Because it composes two signals, it is called CSYNC (Composite SYNC).

These five signals are everything a CRT needs to work.

> **Trivia:** The CRT is purely a signal consumer. It never sends anything "back" on these wires. It is a common misconception that the CRT emits VSYNC. In fact, all signals are generated by the video system.

2.7.1 CRT 101

Because the timing of operations is propagated deep in the GFX system, it is important to understand how a CRT works.

At its core, a CRT is a line-drawing machine. It draws horizontal lines one after another, from left to right and top to bottom. While it scans a line, three analog signals (one for each RGB color) indicate the quantity of electrons to shoot from three guns. The higher the signal, the more electrons shot and the more vivid the color.

On the way toward the panel, electrons are filtered through a shadow mask to make sure they hit the proper type of colored phosphor receptacles which are grouped by three in RGB "slots". The electron beam-slot is not a one to one relationship. The beam can be larger or smaller than a slot.

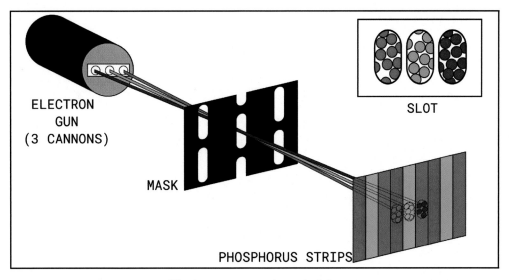

Electron gun, mask, and slots

Slots are not aligned horizontally. When the gun shoots electrons it doesn't really know on which slots they will land. They can hit all in one slot, or two halves of two slots, or other configurations depending on slot density and beam dispersion.

The only guarantees are that an electron from a cannon color lands in a phosphor receptacle of the same color, and that the electron beam height is constant on a line.

A scanline of electron hits wherever

Smaller slots can render the horizontal analog signals with better fidelity.

With this duality of lines and signals, a CRT is both a digital and an analog system. The number of scanlines is finite (i.e: there is a set number of these elements) but there is no horizontal number of "dots", "points", or "pixels" since the three color intensity signals are analog.

2.7.2 Syncing

The RGB signals describe lines to be drawn but the CRT needs to know where to draw them. The control signal allows synchronization of the cannon orientation with the lines' color signal so they are rasterized where they should. Without syncing, the image appears distorted.

A desynced CRT. Lines are correct but not located where they should be

VSYNC signal tells the CRT it should reset the gun's vertical position to 0 at the top of the screen. This motion from bottom to top is called vertical retrace. During the retrace the gun must stop shooting electrons. This is achieved by requesting a black color on the RGB signal. This "blanking" of the RGB lines happens a little bit before and after VSYNC. The total time not drawing anything is called VBLANK.

HSYNC signal tells the CRT that a line has been drawn and the gun's horizontal position should be reset to the left of the screen. This motion is called horizontal retrace. Like the VBLANK, there is a HBLANK timespan.

2.7.3 Fields

The process of drawing scanlines over the screen, also called "raster scan", is incomplete as described. If the gun draws a line and upon HSYNC goes back to the left, it would be drawing the same upper left line over and over again.

It is barely noticeable but scanlines are not drawn straight. There is a slight downward slope. This way, when HSYNC is received and horizontal position is reset, the next line is drawn below the previous.

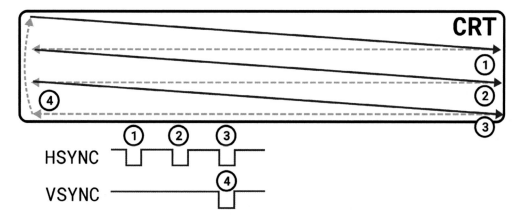

As long as VSYNC is issued at the same time as a HSYNC, the CRT lines are always on the same location on the screen.

In the next drawing, see what happens if VSYNC ③ is issued in the middle of the last line being draw (between HSYNC ② and ④).

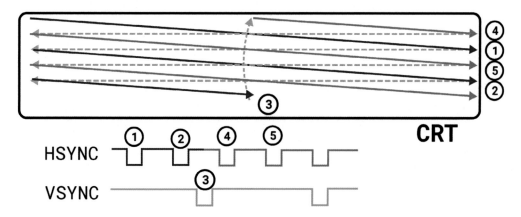

Since only half a line was drawn at the bottom, the gun only progressed down half a space vertically. As a result, the next frame will be interlaced with the previous. This technique is used for TV broadcasts in the USA and Japan via NTSC. A signal carries frames at 30Hz, each contains two "fields" to be drawn interlaced at 60Hz.

While interlacing is acceptable for TV images, it is not for gaming, as the artifacts are disturbingly visible on moving text and sprites.

One solution to this problem is to only use one field and never display anything on the other one. Doing this means designing a video system where VSYNC is always issued along with a HSYNC. The drawback is that since CRTs were built to display interleaved images, they provision for space between lines.

Since this space is not used for another field, the resulting effect is black horizontal strips on the screen. Note that the problem is compensated for by line bleeding so the black lines are not as big as the visible lines.

Non-interlaced scanning show a black space between lines

Besides avoiding interlacing, many other decisions had to be made.

2.7.4 Making Choices

To craft a video system means building a signal generator and a color generator. We'll study the signal generator first. This circuit is built to take an oscillator ticks as input and to output three signals. One signal tells for how long the color generator should hold a color on the color lines, one signal triggers HSYNC, and one signal triggers VSYNC.

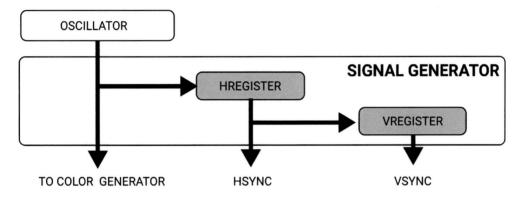

The oscillator feeds an "horizontal register" which increases one by one each tick. Upon reaching its max value, the register wraps around to both issue a HSYNC and increase a "vertical register".

Likewise, when the vertical register reaches its max value, it wraps around and generates a VSYNC.

The color duration has no register counting the ticks. Each tick indicates that a dot is being drawn.

A designer can pick any oscillator frequency (which we call dot-clock from now on). However, they must be careful to choose vertical max value (number of lines) and horizontal max value (number of dots per line) such that vertical frequency and horizontal frequency are compatible with what a CRT can sync on.

As these CRTs of the 90s were meant to TV sets consuming NTSC broadcast so the two imperatives were to be close to **59.95 Hz** VSYNC rate and **15,734 Hz** HSYNC rate.

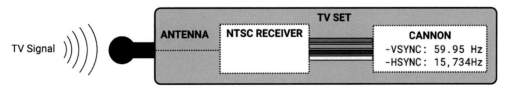

The horizontal frequency and vertical frequency are directly derived from the three values picked for the signal generator. Plugging the numbers into the following formula allows to verify how close a system is from being compatible with a CRT.

$$\text{Horizontal frequency} = \frac{\text{dotclock}}{\text{numDots}}$$

$$\text{Vertical frequency} = \frac{\text{dotclock}}{(\text{numDots} * \text{numLines})}$$

Before looking at Capcom's choices, let's look at the decisions made by video designers for systems contemporary to the CP-System.

	Genesis (H40)[19]	Neo-Geo	Super NES
dots	420	384	341
lines	262	264	262
dot-clock (Hz)	6,711,647	6,000,000	5,369,318
HSYNC frequency (Hz)	15,700	15,625	15,745
VSYNC frequency (Hz)	59,92	59.18	60.09

Signal generator values for Genesis, Neo-Geo, and Super NES

Keep in mind that these resolutions are not what programmers can count on. Because of overhead discussed in the next section, some lines and dots are unavailable. The resolutions presented here are called "overscan resolutions".

Capcom video signal choices

The CPS-1 uses an overscan resolution of `512x262`. The dot-clock is 8 Mhz which is obtained by halving the CPS-A/CPS-B 16 MHz clock (it spares an oscillator chip).

	CP-System
dots	512
lines	262
dot clock (Hz)	8,000,000
HSYNC frequency (Hz)	15,625
VSYNC frequency (Hz)	59.6374

Signal generator values for CP-System

Besides these vertical and horizontal frequency "rules", Capcom engineers had additional constraints. Because the graphic system works with tiles (which we will study in the next section) using sizes of 8, 16, or 32 pens, both axis dimensions had to be multiples of eight.

Blanking

The CP-System overscan resolution of 512x262 seems to indicate a very high resolution for the time. But not all lines and dots on a line can be used, some have to be sacrificed to solve three problems.

First, there is the problem of retracing vertically and horizontally. Cannon movement is not instantaneous, so while it moves horizontally or vertically, it would leave a visible diagonal of electrons across two scanlines (horizontal reset) or across the whole screen (vertical reset).

The second problem is wobbling. Because a reset changes the cannon position abruptly (as opposed to the smooth progression during a scanline), it takes a little bit of time for the electron beam to stabilize again after it completes the reset.

Lastly, the video system needs breaks to read or write data without generating visible artifacts. This includes swapping buffers, updating palette colors, and retrieving the list of sprites/tilemaps to draw on the next scanline.

The solution to these three problems is named blanking. By setting the color signals to zero, the cannon shoots no electrons. Blanking hides artifacts and create a window of time where the video system is inactive. There is a vertical blanking called VBLANK and an horizontal blanking called HBLANK.

Capcom's second set of video signal choices

Out of the 262 total lines available, Capcom decided to use 224 and let VBLANK last for $262 - 224 = 38$ lines. They used 384 dots per line out of 512 total leaving $512 - 384 = 128$ dots to HBLANK. Developers can count on a resolution of 384x224.

	CP-System	Genesis (H40)	Neo-Geo	Super NES
Usable dots	384	320	320	256
HBLANK (dots)	128	100	64	85
Usable lines	224	224	224	224
VBLANK (lines)	38	38	40	38

Usable resolution for CP-System and contemporaries

Pixel Aspect Ratio

The scanlines of a CRT have a fixed height but the width of the dots vary from machine to machine because of their dot-clock. The width/height dot ratio is called the Pixel Aspect Ratio (PAR).

An "ideal" system would have "square" dots with a 1:1 PAR. For these "TV" CRTs built with a set physical scanline height, square pixels were guaranteed if the dot clock was 6,136,363 Hz ($\frac{135}{22}$). A system using a higher frequency would draw narrower dots while a system using a lower frequency would draw wider dots.

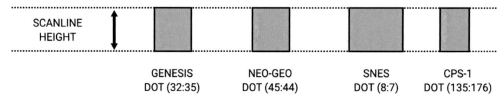

	GENESIS	NEO-GEO	SNES	CPS-1
SCANLINE HEIGHT	DOT (32:35)	DOT (45:44)	DOT (8:7)	DOT (135:176)

Pixel Aspect Ratio of four systems (exaggerated)

Let's look first at the Neo-Geo which has a PAR close to 1:1, resulting in square pixels[20].

Metal Slug as stored in the Neo-Geo ROM, SAR = 320:224

The PAR formula is a simple multiplication by a fraction.

$$PAR = \frac{\text{dotclock MHz}}{\frac{135}{22}} = \frac{\text{dotclock MHz} * 22}{135}$$

The Neo-Geo MVS, with its dot-clock of 6,000,000 Hz has a PAR of 45:44. Combining its 320x240 Storage Aspect Ratio (SAR) with its PAR gives the Display Aspect Ratio (DAR) of the physical image seen on the CRT.

$$\text{Display Aspect Ratio (DAR)} = PAR * SAR = \frac{45 * 320}{44 * 224} = 1.46$$

The near-square pixels result in minimal distortion when the image is presented on a 4:3 CRT. This is very convenient for artists since they can digitize their assets 1:1 and see their artwork rendered as intended.

Metal Slug as it appears on a CRT, DAR = 1.46

The CPS-1 with its resolution of 384x224 and its dot-clock of 8,000,000 Hz results in a PAR of 135:176. Its DAR somewhat matches the CRT aspect ratio of 4:3 (= 1.333).

$$\text{Display Aspect Ratio} = \text{PAR} * \text{SAR} = \frac{135 * 384}{176 * 224} = 1.31$$

However its narrow pixels generate a significant amount of distortion, which was a huge problem for artists. If they digitized their drawings as is, the CRT would present to players a vertically-stretched version of the original vision. As illustrated on page 75, an artist drawing a circular sun on paper, digitizing it as is, and running it via the CPS-1 would see an oval result on the screen.

Akiman reported the problem right away when he started working with the new platform.

> When I was working on my first CPS-1 game, Forgotten Worlds, I noticed the problem of aspect ratio right away.
>
> - "The pixels are not square!" I told my boss.
>
> - "Impossible, I ordered them to be square!" he replied.
>
> He then proceeded to call hardware on the spot.
>
> - "The pixels are square!" he added.
>
> Later I protested again to which my boss replied it was a calculation error.
>
> — Akiman, Lead Artist [11]

Could it have been an oversight? Could it actually be a calculation error? In all likelihood the hardware designers wanted to give the CPS-1 a very high horizontal resolution to make it competitive, even if this meant making artists' lives a little bit difficult.

Artists managed to work around this annoying "feature" by drawing their assets pre-stretched (as seen on 76). Their process is elaborated on page 143.

In the rest of the book, the format of images will vary. For real-estate reasons, the "screenshot" may be shown with SAR proportions or DAR proportions depending on the needs. The same goes with the drawings. Since the difference is pretty significant between squares and rectangles (as seen on page 76), aspect ratio is not mentioned again.

SAR (as intended by artist)

DAR (distorded)

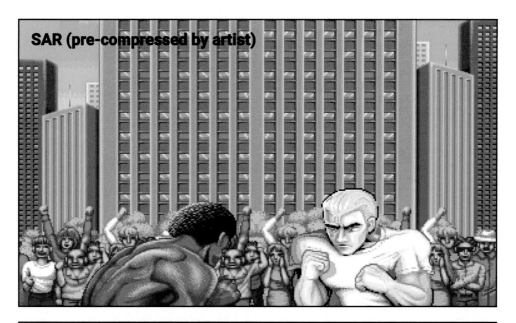

Trivia: The designers of R-Type at Irem were unsatisfied with the default "standard" 224 usable lines of a CRT.

They calibrated their M72-System registers to draw 284 lines, 512 dots, and used an 8 Mhz dot-clock. Leaving 128 dots to HBLANK and 28 lines to VBLANK resulted in a resolution of 384x256 which was higher than other arcade titles at the time.

The trade-off was a vertical refresh rate of 55.017605 Hz which was visually less pleasing and dangerously 10% off from the CRT recommended values. This refresh rate is difficult to replicate for "modern" emulators but what an impressive feat for a 1987 system!

2.7.5   Color Space

Before moving to the color generator, a characteristic to decide on was the color depth.

The CPS-1 uses 16 bits to encode colors with 4 bits per RGB component for a total of 12 bits allowing 4,096 colors.

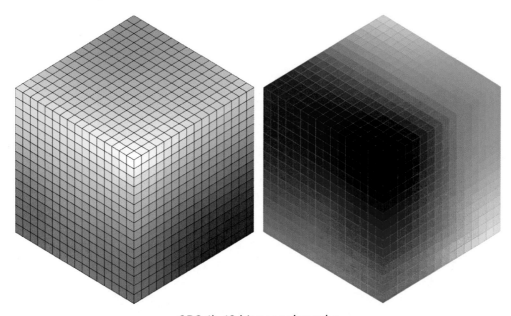

CPS-1's 12-bit per color cube

The four remaining bits express brightness to allow 16 shades of a base color. In total, 65,536 different colors are available to artists.

0	1	2	3	4	5	6	7	8	9	A	B	C	D	E	F

All darker shades of red using a `{0xF,0x0, 0x0}` base.

2.7.6 Putting it All Together

Knowing how a CRT works and what decisions Capcom engineers made, we can now understand the video signal timings.

With a "pixel" clock coming from the GFX oscillator (16MHz) halved to 8MHz, a color is issued every 1s / 8MHz = 125ns.

The horizontal resolution of 512 mandates a HSYNC to be generated every 512 * 0.125 = 64μs. The resulting refresh rate is 8MHz / (512x262) = 59.637Hz and a VSYNC is issued every 1000ms/59.637 = 16.7ms.

A summary drawing exposes all timing and regions, as well as the significant part of the image not usable due to horizontal and vertical blanking.

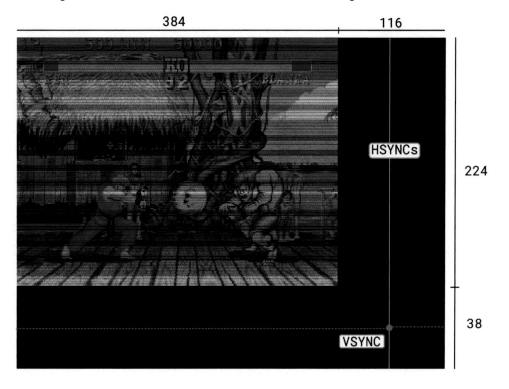

Keep in mind that HSYNC happens 262 times (green vertical lines) but VSYNC occurs only once. The dashed horizontal red line in the previous drawing is only here to represent where the electron gun resets to the top of the screen.

The sheer amount of black in the drawings shows the extent of the overhead associated with beam wobbling management. But the time spent not drawing is not wasted. It is leveraged to perform background operations such as modifying palette colors. e.g: Sixteen lines are necessary for a palette page (32 palettes) "upload".

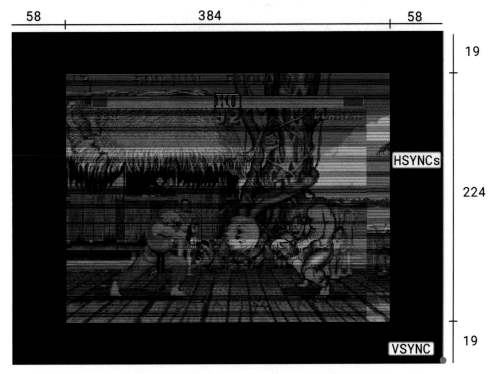

Same concept but closer to what happen in CRT screen space

2.7.7   Color Generator

To generate color signals, the CPS-1 uses a palette system storing colors via 4 x 2Ki x 1B `CXK5814P-35L` SRAM chips.

These memory elements feature pinouts explained earlier like Power `+5V`, Ground `GND`, Addresses `A0-A10`, Data `D0-D7`, Write (`WE`), Read (`OW`), and Chip Enabled (`CE`).

What is uncanny is that the component connected to the address lines is not the one connected to the data lines.

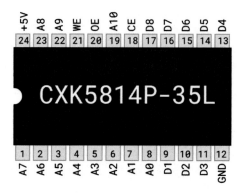

The CPS-B drives the address bus at 8MHz to generate the DAC 16-bit inputs, which in turn generates three analog Red, Green, and Blue signals. In parallel, it generates the HSYNC and VSYNC signals, composited into CSYNC.

Notice how one line out of twelve is used not for addressing but for CE ing chip pairs.

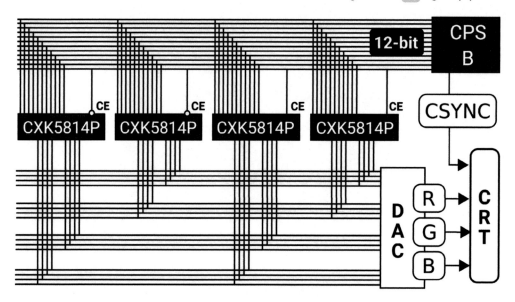

Colors are grouped into palettes containing 16 units. As will be studied later, the GFX system features 6 layers and each of them allows 32 palettes (called page). This brings the total to 6*32*15 = 2,880 colors which requires 12-bit to be indexed.

The palette SRAM chips are nearly constantly used to generate colors. Their content can only be modified during VBLANK.

Twelves palettes from the characters of a famous Capcom fighting game. Can you recognize them?

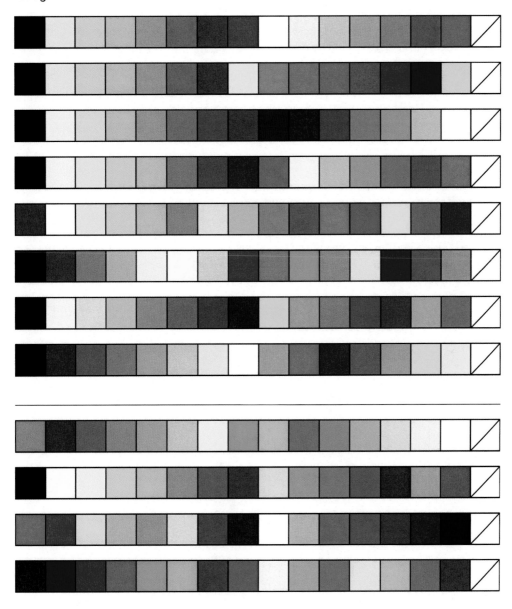

Hint: RKCHGZBD-BVSB.

2.8 Graphic System

The graphic system is the most complicated to understand in the whole machine. It is complex because it must satisfy three demanding systems.

On one side, there is Control which requests an elaborate composition of backgrounds and sprites to appear on the screen. The description is much more verbose than a simple integer received by the Sound system to play a sample or a music. Communication happens by not only exposing the graphic registers, but also sharing access to a shared memory called "GFX RAM". Control's m68k writes "draw commands" which the GFX system reads and executes.

On the other side is the 8 MHz Video system which mercilessly demands a pixel color every 125ns. The CRT cannons never wait and a color must be issued on the dot, no matter what.

Finally there is the GFXROM, a huge repository of up to 12MiB graphic assets. It has a finite latency and throughput which cannot satisfy the Video systems if it were to work on a per-pixel request/response.

Solving these problems of timing and latency well is what made the CPS-1 stand out. It is inarguably the "secret sauce" of the system.

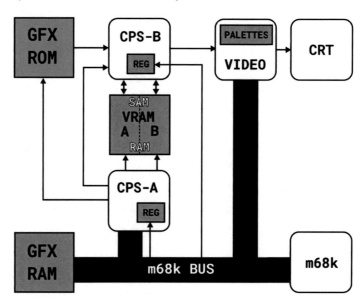

Architecture of the CPS-1 Graphic System

2.8.1   CPS-A and CPS-B: The ASICs powerhouse

To build their rendering pipeline, Capcom did not rely on another company's product. They crafted their own **A**pplication-**S**pecific **I**ntegrated **C**ircuit (ASIC), tailored to their needs, the CPS-A (the brain) and CPS-B (the legs).

2.8.2   Pens and Inks

The elementary unit of work is a 4-bit value which is an index into a 16 colors palette. Everything, from backgrounds to sprites, uses these 4-bit nibble indexes. A good analogy, and the terminology used in this book, is to picture the GFX manipulating "pens" (palette indexes). The color to appear on the screen is decided not by the pen but by the value at this index, which is called "ink".

This division makes the GFX system unaware of the color that will appear to players on the CRT since it only manipulates pens.

Groups of four bytes encoding 8 pens are "tile lines". When combined vertically, they make a "tile", the elementary unit manipulated by background and sprite layers.

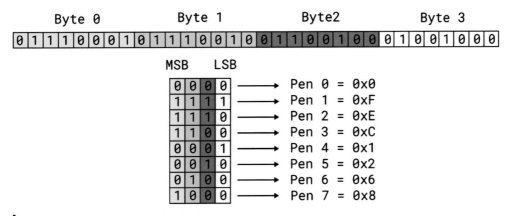

Trivia: Pen value `0xF` is always treated as transparent!

2.8.3   Elements of drawing

Games are made of backgrounds on top of which are drawn sprites. The easiest to implement are the background circuits. They are studied first, followed by the sprite circuits.

2.8.4 Drawing background

A background is described in terms of "tiles", whose arrangement is described in a map. The goal of the circuit is to "rasterize" the map of tiles (called "tilemap").

A naive design would work at the same speed as the video system (8MHz). For each pixel (every 125ns) the GFXRAM would be read to know what tile to display. Then a pen would be retrieved from the GFXROM. Finally that pen would be sent to the palette system where the color would be converted by the video DAC.

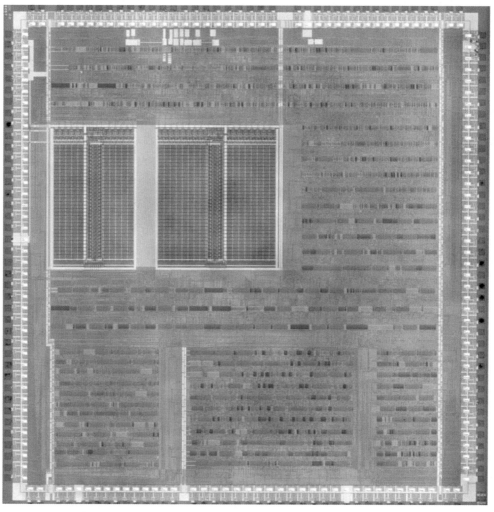

CPS-A die. Notice the real estate dedicated to GFXRAM caching

Even though the machine uses the fastest type of memory (SRAM), its response time does not permit enough roundtrips. This problem is solved via caching, streaming, channeling, and a humongous (for the time) 32-bit GFXROM/CPS-B local data bus.

Caching

The CPS-A only accesses the GFXRAM during the HBLANK interval. To eliminate memory read operations while a scanline is rasterized, a line's worth of tilemap is retrieved and stored in an internal cache of 256 entries. Each entry stores 16-bit tileID + 10-bit attributes. Notice the two parts on the die storing respectively 10 bits and 16 bits.

Streaming

Pen values are streamed from GFXROM to the CRT without intermediate storage. The GFXROM data is retrieved eight pens at a time thanks to a 32-bit data bus.

The system works with the GFXROM address lines connected to the CPS-A (with intermediate PAL decoding). The data lines are connected to the CPS-B where pen values are selected/discarded before being sent to the video system.

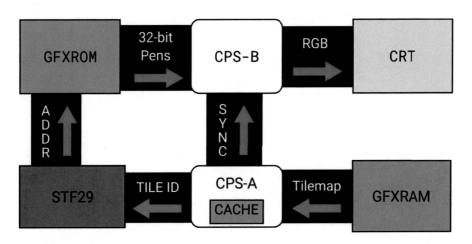

Channels

To further improve response time, the GFXROM data uses a layout where 8 consecutive bytes are interleaved 16 bits at a time across four chips.

Upon reading, an address is issued to two chips at the same time, but their data lines are enabled consecutively. Channeling avoids one "fetch time" every two reads.

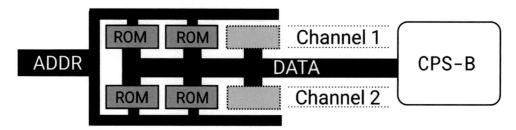

2.8.5 CPS1 Tilemaps

The CPS-1 features three tilemap layers named SCROLL1, SCROLL2, and SCROLL3. They all rely on tilemaps made of 64x64 tiles.

Street Fighter 2

SCROLL1 uses tiles of dimensions 8x8 resulting in a total dimension of 512x512. SCROLL2 uses tiles of dimensions 16x16 resulting in a total dimension of 1024x1024. SCROLL3 uses tiles of dimensions 32x32 resulting in a total dimension of 2048x2048.

Each tilemap has a maximum capacity of 32 palettes (called a palette page) which any tile can use freely. SCROLLS can be offset ("scrolled", hence their name) by any X or Y value, appear in any order, and be used for any purpose.

In Street Fighter 2, three scrolls are used to improve parallax. The GUI elements are rendered alongside the sprites on a fourth layer called "OBJ" which is studied later.

Other titles such as the shoot'em up Forgotten Worlds required all the sprites the machine could provide for the gameplay. To avoid wasting any of them, the GUI is drawn on SCROLL1 instead of OBJ. The trade-off is that GUI elements are aligned on a 8-pixel grid which is a minor inconvenience.

Color codes used in this section are ■ SCROLL1, ■ SCROLL2, ■ SCROLL3, ■ OBJ.

Street Fighter 2 layers

Starfields

Besides SCROLLs, the CPS-1 has two "STARfield" layers which are always behind the
SCROLLs and always in order STAR1 then STAR2. Like the other layers, one full page
of 32 palettes is available to each of them.

To render the stars, the GFXROM contains no tiles but instead bytecode dictating the
position of points as well as palette cycling timing.

It is surprising nowadays to see so much silicon dedicated to a "niche" feature, but the
extreme popularity of shoot em ups like R-Type, Gradius, or Darius at the time made
a good case for it. Designing a system saving both considerable GFXROM space and
artists' time was a good idea at the time. Ironically, the platform ended up receiving no
space shooter!

That did not prevent the feature from being used, though. Long after STARfields went
out of fashion, the system was re-purposed.

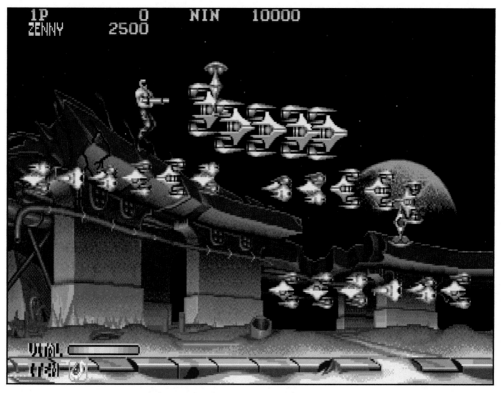

Forgotten Worlds. Notice the GUI elements grid alignment (SCROLL1)

Noir Black

When designers needed a full black background, instead of using a SCROLL and repeatedly requesting rows of black tiles to cover the whole screen, they only had to use a STARfield and request no stars.

This is the unacknowledged poetry of the Street Fighter Hyper Fighting intro sequence. As the title appears, the black background is in fact a pitch black night sky which nobody ever knew about.

> **Trivia:** The layer system does not use a painter algorithm where pixels are written over and over in a framebuffer. The CPS-B receives a stream of all layers' pens which are selected based on the layer priority and transparency value (`0xF`). Once selected, the pen value is forwarded directly to the video system.

Layers color codes, ■ SCROLL1, ■ SCROLL2, ■ SCROLL3, □ STAR1, □ STAR2, ■ OBJ.

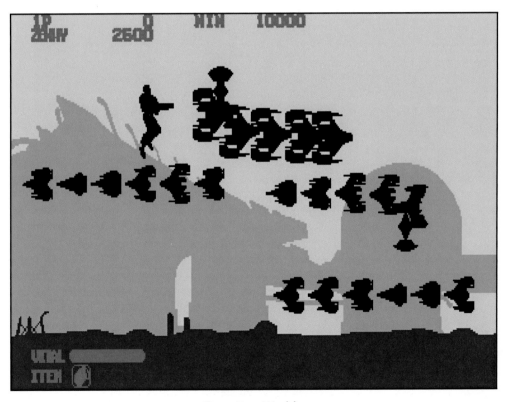

Forgotten Worlds

Draw order and Priority mask

The drawing order (also called "priority") of SCROLLs and the sprite layer are entirely configurable (excluding the STARs which must remain behind). Any order can be requested but there is an extra feature available to the SCROLL drawn just behind the sprite layer.

Take the example of Final Fight. After fighting their way to a busy subway, Haggar and Guy find themselves exiting the train station to continue happily brawling in a desolated part of the city.

As they are going up the stairs, observe the "back to front" order the following layers.

- ■ SCROLL3 used for the skyline.
- □ SCROLL2 used for the main playground.
- ■ OBJ for the main characters, tires, and barrel sprites.
- □ On top of everything, SCROLL1 for the GUI.

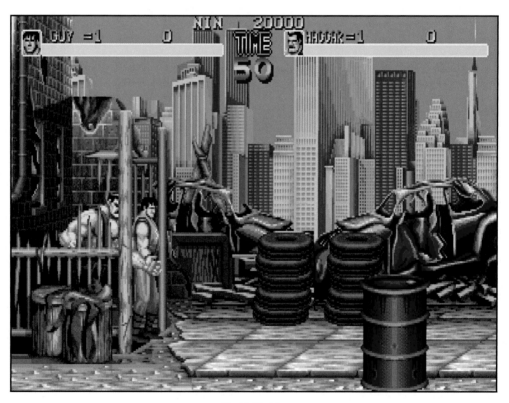

Final Fight

It all makes sense except for one detail. If we look closely at Haggar (for those who never played Final Fight, Haggar is the bigger one of the two) something is off since it appears to be both in front and behind SCROLL2.

The CPS-B allows the SCROLL layer behind the OBJs to tag each of its tiles with a single priority group ID (from a choice of four groups). In each of these groups, sixteen bits indicate which pen in the tile palette have precedence over OBJ.

This is how Final Fight characters are sandwiched by SCROLL2. The tiles making the "near" portion of the ramp are tagged to use two priority mask groups. The "wood" tile use the group mask 0 to make pens resulting in colors ☐, ■, ■, and ■ being given precedence. Likewise, the garbage tiles are tagged with group 1 to give precedence to eight pens resulting in colors ■, ■, ☐, ■, ■, ■, ■ and ■.

Once the exit animation is over, all tiles priority groups are cleared to allow free roaming (except behind the ramp) and brawling over the whole screen without priority concerns.

Refer to the CPS-B API on page 199 for more details about tagging and masking.

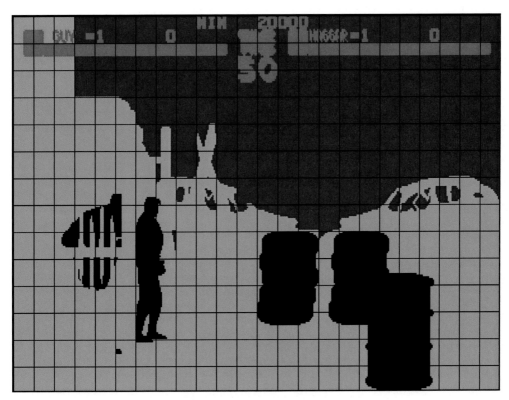

Final Fight with SCROLL2 layer grid

Rowscrolling

SCROLL 2 has the ability to horizontally offset rows based on their vertical position.

This capability, commonly known as "rowscroll", is implemented via a table of 1024 10-bit integers (one for each line) in GFXRAM.

This is a feature completely hard-coded in the ASICs. Once requested, the m68k is uninvolved, it has no awareness of HSYNC, only VSYNC is known.

> I knew we had raster scrolling so I talked with the programmers and we gave it a shot. It was effective. However, to this day I have no idea about what's going on under the hood!
>
>   — Nin

Street Fighter 2, Ryu's floor is rowscrolled

Choosing features

The starfield and rowscroll features are good examples of how difficult it is to design hardware. Doing it well consists of accurately predicting what will be useful and what won't.

While starfields were heavily used in the inaugural title, "Forgotten Worlds", and prominently featured in the second one , "Strider", rowscroll on the other hand saw no usage for nearly two years.

Relegated to implementing flame effects in "Magic Sword" and hazy backgrounds in "Carrier Air Wing", rowscrolling barely appeared for a few seconds of gameplay in the five titles [15] it was featured in.

Ultimately, the balance of these two features was reversed when rowscroll was used to implement the notoriously beautiful per-line floor parallax in Street Fighter 2, massively contributing to the graphic appeal of the game.

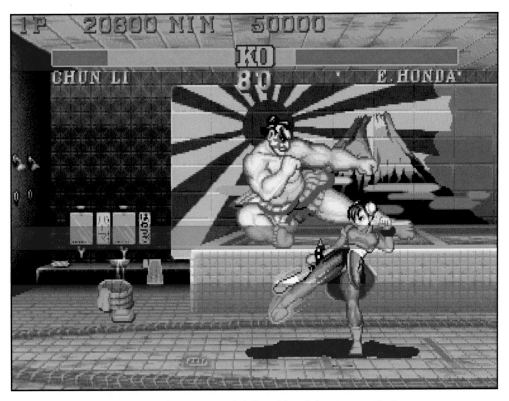

Street Fighter 2, Honda's level is triple rowscrolled

Pushing the Limits

Besides priority mask, tiles can be flipped horizontally and/or vertically but there is no scaling or rotation. Moreover, the CPU has no access to the VRAM which forbids pixel "plotting". That did not prevent seemingly impossible effects from being achieved.

In Ghouls 'n Ghosts' first level, on top of hordes of zombies, a Red Arremer, and unforgiving controls, the player must face the weather. Wind picks up and soon after heavy rains. If you look at the screenshot of the layer below, most layers are used and no rain should be possible.

- ▨ STAR1 used for the dark sky.
- ▪ SCROLL3 used for background.
- ▨ SCROLL2 used for playground.
- ▪ OBJ for the main character, big rain drops, and enemies.
- ▨ On top of everything, SCROLL1 for the GUI.

Ghouls 'n Ghosts with GUI

To add rainfall, developers leveraged temporal blending on the same layer as the GUI. Every five frames the GUI is not drawn. Instead a full screen of rain tiles is rendered, resulting in a convincing effect. Temporal blending is often used to fake translucency.

Plotting Pixels

The introduction sequence of the shoot'em up Carrier Air Wing (page 96 and 97) is even more impressive. As a F-14 Tomcat takes off from its carrier, the jet leaves in its trail an exhaust that expands vertically one pixel line at a time. The gaze then disperses with a fizzlefade effect.

It seems like pixels are plotted into a framebuffer but both effects are rendered via the OBJ layer (■). Exhaust expansion is done with 16 pre-rendered tiles (each covering more vertical lines). The fizzlefade is achieved with titles featuring an increasing density of transparent pens. The fizzle repeating pattern is visible on the fourth color coded screenshot.

Ghouls 'n Ghosts when rain falls

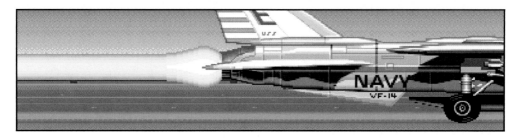

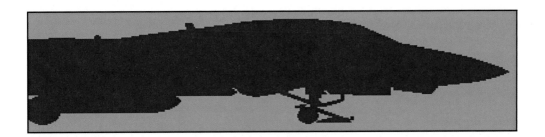

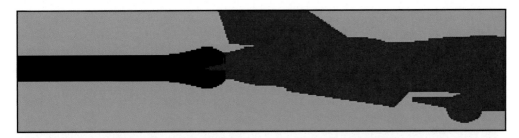

2.8.6 Drawing Sprites

Drawing sprites is more difficult than drawing tilemaps. It involves solving the same problems of bandwidth and latency, only sprites can appear anywhere on the screen and are not aligned on a grid.

In order to fully appreciate how Capcom solved this problem, it is worth understanding how other platforms tackled it.

Hardware sprites

A sprite circuit can be implemented using the same logic as a tilemap. It is a special case where the map features a single tile and no horizontal or vertical scrolling is allowed.

Every HSYNC, the GFXRAM is read to know if a sprite appears on the next scanline. If it does, the circuit makes sure to intercept tilemap pens to issue sprite pens instead.

It is an approach that comes with two drawbacks. First, it requires one circuit per sprite which is expensive. Second, the one-to-one complexity makes it impossible to scale to more than a few units. Nonetheless, this is the solution used by machines such as the Commodore 64 which advertised their circuitry as "hardware sprites".

As limiting as it sounds there is a bit of flexibility thanks to a technique known as multiplexing. A C64 has 8 sprite "units" but that does not mean it can only draw eight sprites on the whole screen. It only means it can only draw eight sprites on the same scanline.

As the CRT cannon progresses down the screen, a sprite unit used above can be reused to draw sprites located below. By changing the configuration during HBLANK, many more than eight sprites can be drawn. This trick was extensively used in games to reach well over 100 sprites on screen.

Likewise, by using built-in multiplexing, the Commodore Amiga placed an horizontal limit of 8 pixels for its sprites' width but allowed unlimited height.

Line buffer

To scale better and increase the number of sprites supported, hardware designers introduced the concept of line buffers.

A line buffer system requires a buffer as wide as a visible line on the CRT. The buffer is populated with pen codes by a Pixel Processing Unit. The number of sprites, scale and rotation capabilities depends on how much work the PPU is able to do.

The limiting factor is that the line buffer can be written only during HBLANK ($16\mu s$) since it is used the rest of the time to feed the CRT.

Systems like the Super Nintendo use a line buffer with an impressive PPU resulting in breathtaking fullscreen visual effects involving Mode-7/HDMA. This particularly shone in games like F-Zero or Pilot Wings.

Double Line buffer

A straight forward way to make a GFX more powerful is to simply give it more time to do its jobs. The merciless pixel clock cannot be cheated but the pipeline can be made deeper.

By using two line buffers alternately, the GFX pipeline is made deeper which increases its latency but also frees itself from rendering only during HBLANK. While a line buffer is fed to the video, another one is rendered. This allows drawing during one full scanline ($64\mu s$) and a GFX four times more capable than one using a single line buffer.

This choice, made by SNK for its Neo-Geo, allowed gorgeous titles such as "Metal Slug" to be built entirely with sprites without using tilemaps.

This technique is so powerful that the entire Neo-Geo rendering pipeline revolves around its double line buffer system. It needs no tilemap system.

CPS1 Sprite FrameBuffer

Capcom engineers wanted something even more powerful than a double line buffer. To allow more time than the $64\mu s$ granted by a double line buffer, the CPS-1 was built around a double sprite framebuffer (the same technology as Sega Super Scaler). To host these framebuffers, the machine uses a dedicated memory called VRAM.

With a double sprite framebuffer, the PPU does not just draw a line in advance but a whole screen. This technique averages 16% more time per line for the graphic chip to do its work, and more importantly it allows any number of tiles per line (even the powerful Neo-Geo has a limit of 96 tiles per line).

The gain is massive but it comes with three drawbacks.

Price tag

First, the price of the machine goes up since it requires much more buffering capacity. At the resolution of 384*224, 9 bits per pixel are stored (5-bit palette index + 4-bit color index) requiring 200 KiB of storage for two framebuffers.

Bandwidth requirements

The second impact is on the bus. A massive amount of data is now written and read to/from the VRAM. It requires so much bandwidth that an especially large data bus connecting the GFX pipeline and the VRAM must be designed.

De-synchronization

Lastly, there is the problem of tilemap and sprite synchronization. When the m68k writes a layout in the GFXRAM, the graphic system picks it up but routes background tiles and sprite tiles to different locations. The tilemap is rasterized directly towards the video system while the sprite layer is rendered to the VRAM framebuffer where it will be picked up on the next frame.

> **Trivia:** The sync issue is particularly noticeable in Final Fight level 2. The subway wagon moves up and down to simulate rail junction bumps, but the handles on the ceiling and the characters appear to lag behind.

A three-frame sequence is enough to illustrate the issue. On frame 1, the scrolls of frame 1 are displayed. No sprites are visible at that point.

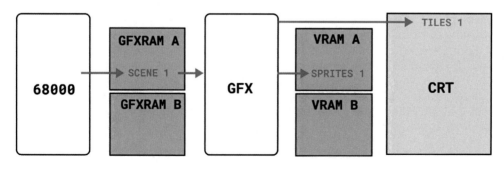

Frame 1

Next, the scrolls of frame 2 are displayed along with the spritebuffer from frame 1.

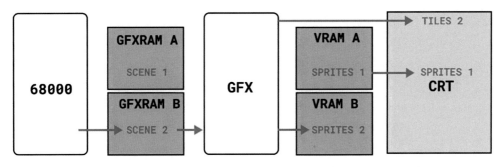

Frame 2

Finally, the scrolls of frame 3 are displayed along with the spritebuffer from frame 2. The desyncing can only be compensated in software by drawing OBJs one frame ahead of SCROLLs.

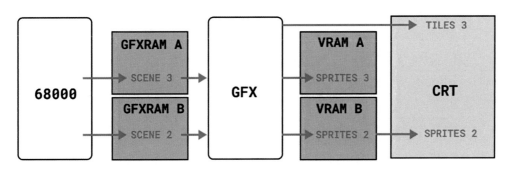

Frame 3

CPS1 Sprites Tile

With its architecture based on a double sprite framebuffer, Capcom built a powerful system able to move an immense volume of sprites. But performance was only one part of the equation. They also had to come up with a flexible way for artists to use it.

Up to that point, frustration arose from sprite dimensions (all sprites had to have the same sizes), shapes (mandatory rectangular), and colors (one palette per sprite).

The CPS-1 lifted these three limitations by abandoning the concept of sprites. The CPS-1 does have a "sprite" layer but it is made of tiles of dimensions 16x16 pixels. Called OBJ (for OBJects) its TILEs can be arranged however an artist requires to build sprites of arbitrary shapes and sizes.

Like the other layers, OBJ palette page features 32 units which any tile can freely use.

Street Fighter II demonstrates the power of the tile system. Combining them creates a universe of rich characters with specific shapes, giving them more personality.

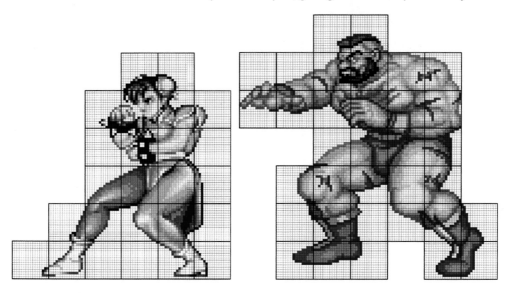

Chunli guard pose, 25 tiles (3,200 bytes). Zangief standing, 34 tiles (4,352 bytes).

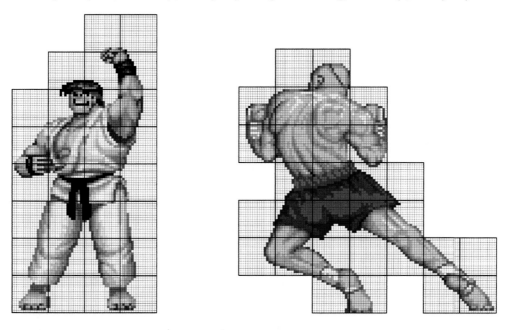

Ryu victory pose, 29 tiles (3,712 bytes). Sagat Tiger Punch pose, 30 tiles (3,840 bytes).

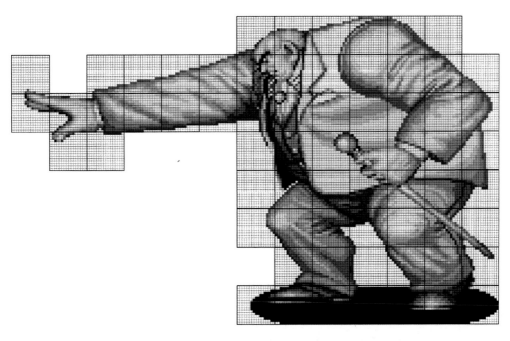

The ultimate boss in "The Punisher", Kingpin, is a mountain of a man made of 69 tiles, which covers half the screen. This impressive feat came with minimal "wasted" pixels thanks to the usage of composed tiles.

Tiles in the OBJ layer have attributes allowing them to be rendered horizontally and/or vertically flipped. However there is still no support for rotation or scaling.

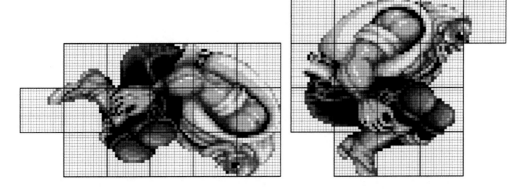

When Final Fight's mini-boss, Damned, does a back-flip in level 1, no rotation is performed. Two sets of tiles are used and X/Y flipped to generate two extra mirrored sets. The effect works with four poses, thanks to fast movements and players' brain interpolation.

2.8.7   OBJ Limitations

The sprite system has a hard limit of 256 tiles per frame. This is not an arbitrary number since the constraint is dictated by how many tiles the system is able to read from the GFXROM and write to the VRAM during a full CRT raster scan (16.7ms).

Because OBJ tiles are the most versatile (they can be placed independently and anywhere on the screen), it was tempting to use them often.

Street Fighter II designers pushed the machine to the edge of its limits by using OBJ tiles not only for opponents, arena decoration, GUI, but also to embellish the background parallax effect. This led to problems when a sequel was in the making.

When Ken faces Ryu in Japan, nearly 200 tiles are used. If two of the biggest contestants, Honda and Zangief, were to face each other on this stage, the CPS-1 would be unable to render all OBJ tiles necessary. Such configuration was impossible in "Street Fighter 2" but became a feature of "Street Fighter 2: Champion Edition", which allowed mirror opponents to face each other in any location.

We carefully planned SF2 so that the biggest character and the second biggest character could just barely fit on screen at the same time.

But when mirror matches became possible in Champion Edition, that meant that we had to be able to display two copies of the biggest character on screen.

We ended up having to remove background elements and such.

— Nin

To remain within the OBJ budget, the "wind, forest, fire, mountain" ("風林火山") sign was removed. All other breakables (Ken's barrel, Guile's crate, and Dictator's statues) were allowed to remain.

Trivia: Decorations in Street Fighter 2 were the object of much consideration. The stone on the ground in Sagat's stage randomly moves at the beginning of each round so it cannot be used as a landmark by players.

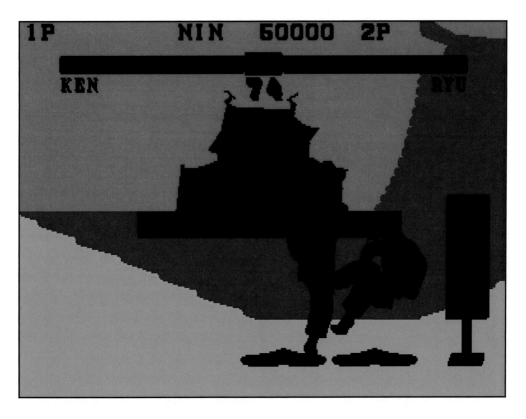

Going Too Far

Games were tested to ensure the OBJ budget was not exceed but Final Fight's last level (Bay Area) managed to ship with that very problem. When the heroes encounter an unprecedented level of opposition, the list of sprites is as follows[27].

- Haggar and Cody.
- Two standing barrels and two rolling barrels.
- Three Axl (grey heavy) (two flying backward).
- Three Slash (copper heavy) (two temporarily KOed).
- One Bred (grey minion) and one Dug (red minion).
- Dirt raised by the rolling barrels.

This scene has 258 tiles on the OBJ layer. Final Fight engine is smart enough to not render partial sprites. Since Haggar, the last sprite on the list, pushes the total 2 tiles past the maximum, all its tiles are dropped.

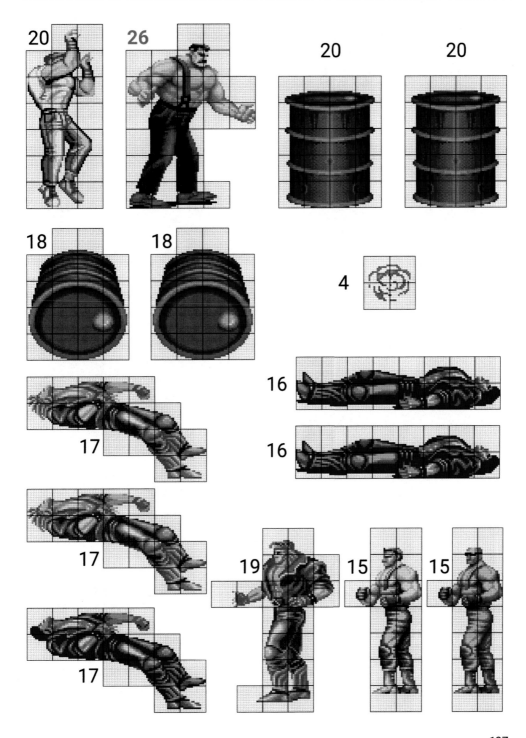

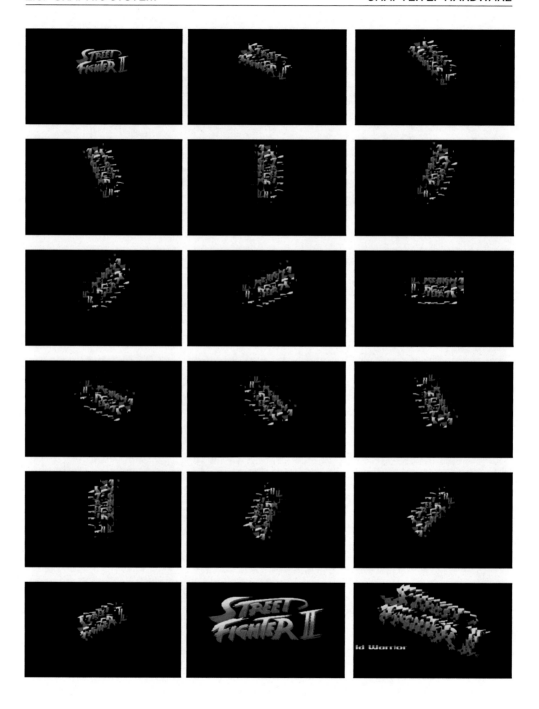

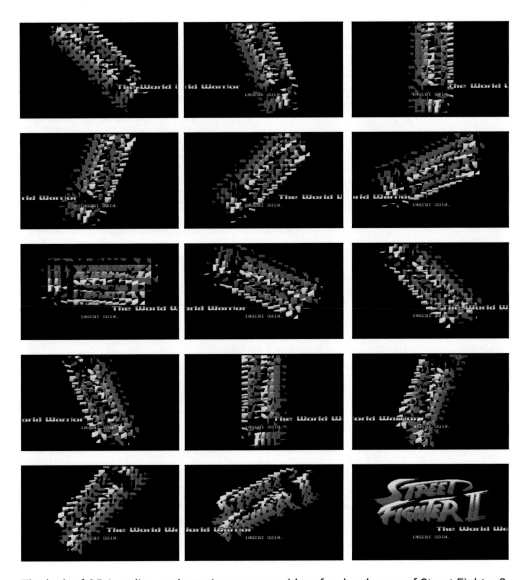

The lack of OBJ scaling and rotation was a problem for developers of Street Fighter 2 as the intro needed precisely these two operations.

To fake it, two logos are used, a small one made of 33 tiles and a large one made of 112 tiles. Tiles move on a circular pattern revolving around the center of the shape. The small to large substitution happens at the end of the first revolution.

Once again, Capcom banked on fast movement, brain interpolation, and maybe forgiveness due to a damn good game.

The World Warrier

The OBJ system was used in a creative way by Akiman to solve a show-stopper bug when he was working as a planner for Street Fighter 2.

> Just three days before the deadline, I discovered something horrible.
>
> I had made a mistake with the subtitle "World Warrior", mis-spelling it "World Warrier."
>
> — Akiman

The subtitle was drawn with the OBJ layer, using 16 draw calls pointing to tileID `0x0`, `0x1`, `0x2`, `0x3`, `0x4`, `0x5`, `0x6`, `0x7`, `0x8`, `0x9`, `0xA`, `0xB`, `0xC`, `0xD`, `0xE`, `0xE`.

Looking inside the GFXROM, one can find the 16 tiles making the "World Warrier".

`0x0 0x1 0x2 0x3 0x4 0x5 0x6 0x7 0x8 0x9 0xA 0xB 0xC 0xD 0xE 0xF`

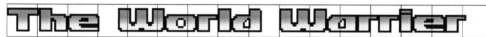

The 16 OBJ tiles making the title, with a typo

> It was several months after all the sprite work had been done. Since the logo had already been created, I couldn't just go in and change the letter at this point.
>
> — Akiman

What Akiman describe is that the GFXROM and all the tiles in it had been finalized. However they could still make modification to the 68000 instructions and most importantly, the palettes that were stored along with it.

> "Maybe I can just force it to look like an 'o'," I thought. I tried layering various other sprites over it until finally, it looked like an 'o'.
>
> Phew!
>
> — Akiman

A recreation of the problem

How in the wORld, do you make an 'e' looks like an 'o'? It turns out that Akiman was lucky in the mistake he had made since the letters he needed, 'o' and 'r', can be found in the word "World".

Akiman leveraged what was available and changed the 68000 draw calls to drop the three last tiles and instead draw again tiles `0x6` and `0x7` at the end.

It only partially solved the problem since the split 'W' looked like an 'I' which made the title read "The World Warrlor".

0x0 0x1 0x2 0x3 0x4 0x5 0x6 0x7 0x8 0x9 0xA 0xB 0xC 0x5 0x6

"The World Warrlor". A little bit better

The problem was displaced from turning an 'e' into an 'o', to turning an 'I' into and 'i'. That would have been simple if the CPU could have written in the VRAM but as we have seen these chips are not mapped in the m68k address space.

There is an expensive way to fake pixel plotting. The idea is to find a tile almost fully transparent (0xF) but with only a single pen value set in it.

Akiman found just that in one of Guile's poses. His calf met these criteria with a simple pen value in its lower left.

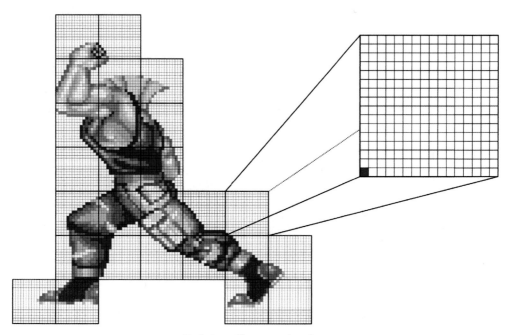

Guile's calf saves the day

Using Guile's calf as a pencil, but with the title's palette, three tiles are drawn over the 'I' to split it into an 'i'.

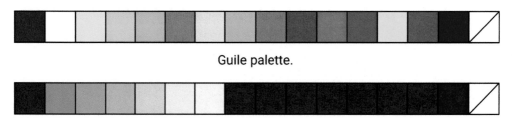

Guile palette.

Title palette.

In a troubling coincidence, the pen corresponding colors were a match.

18 draw calls. Three more than necessary but with proper spelling.

Once you see it, you can't unsee it

2.8.8   Putting it All Together

We now have enough knowledge to fully understand how the CPS-A and CPS-B cooperate to render graphics.

The two graphics chips closely work together by sharing custody of the GFX ROM and VRAM.

The CPS-A generates four interleaved streams of pens (OBJ, SCR1, SR2, and SRC3) by driving the address bus. The CPS-B receives the data and decides for each "pixel" which stream is visible.

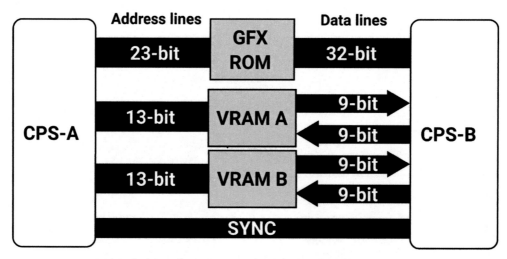

CPS-A (address) and CPS-B (data) GFX ROM/VRAM lines

Besides deciding source and destination of data, the CPS-A also generates LI: (Line increment) and FI: (Frame increment) towards the CPS-B where they are turned into HSYNC and VSYNC for the CRT.

The 23-bit address line to the GFX ROM is special. It is not a raw address but a layerID + tileID within that layer. The PAL STF29 converts IDs into addresses.

The CPS-B is put under heavy contribution. It must simultaneously write the next sprite framebuffer but also render the current by reading the previous sprite framebuffer and sampling all five other layers.

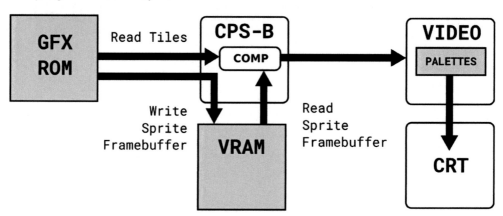

To keep up with bandwidth requirements, the VRAM and GFX ROM systems are specifically crafted with wide data lines.

VRAM

The VRAM system is physically split via two independent blocks, A and B, to facilitate sprite buffer double buffering. This component also benefits from an exceptionally powerful chip compared to the rest of the machine.

A quick glance at the HM53461P shows the usual +5V, GND, CLK, and address/data pins. However SD0, SD1, SD2, and SD3 indicate this chip does more than the ones we have seen so far.

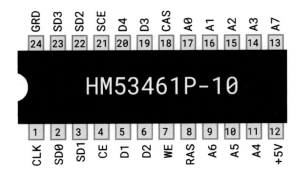

Able to store 65,536 Ki x 4-bit, the HM53461P is peculiar because it not only features a RAM port (D1–D4), it also features a SAM "serial" port (SD1–SD4).

The RAM port is accessed "normally" by first asserting the address lines along with the control lines and then reading or writing on the data lines.

The SAM port is different. Upon asserting the address lines, an internal buffer is latched. Each subsequent control operation automatically increments the address counter.

This design would allow RAM and SAM to be accessed simultaneously but this never happens. When A is read, B is written and the other way around. The real value is in the access time. If the RAM port's 100ms is a "normal" figure, the SAM port read operations complete more than twice as fast, taking only 40ms.

This is a perfect component for a system that needs to write a few values at varying locations (like when the CPS-B renders a sprite buffer) but read a very large amount sequentially (like when the CPS-B must compose pens towards the palette system).

On the Street Fighter II board, twelve HM53461P are combined into six pairs, resulting in 384 KiB. Four chips are used for a single line so 96 KiB is never used.

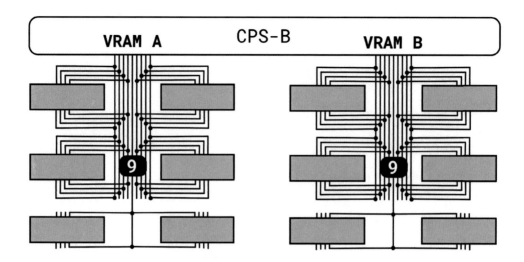

GFX ROM

To keep up with the much higher storage requirements, the GFX ROM system is not designed like the others.

While other chips on the board-B are `27C010` and `27C512`, the GFXROM is made of `MB834200B` (256 Ki x 16-bit). This type of ROM has a much higher capacity but also a slower access time (150ns).

It is likely the dual-channel architecture is the result of a combined desire to use inexpensive components to keep the price down while maintaining high performance.

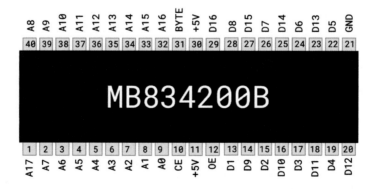

On the Street Fighter II board, twelve `MB834200B-15` are combined for a total of 6 MiB of GFX assets.

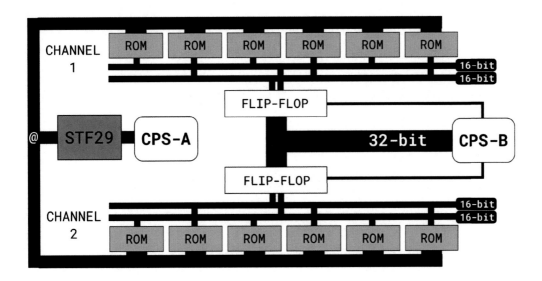

2.9 Copy Protection System

Upon release, Capcom CEO Kenzo Tsujimoto was confident the CPS-1 would significantly reduce piracy, even going as far as labeling it "impossible to copy".

> The new CP System arcade boards are very important to Capcom in two regards. First, they have much more memory than our previous hardware. Game developers will have free reign to explore new, exciting design ideas and take advantage of the latest technological developments. The CP System has upped the level of our developers already.
>
> The second big thing is copy protection. Illegal bootlegs have been a huge problem for us overseas; I believe the CP System is the only PCB hardware today that cannot be copied. The boards contain various copy protection methods, and their advanced hardware should make it difficult for bootleggers seeking to create knockoffs with today's components.
>
> Bootlegs don't only hurt us; they're also a nuisance for our customers who think they are getting a genuine board. We see copy protection as one of the main achievements of the CP System.
>
> — Kenzo Tsujimoto, Capcom CEO [26]

There were good reasons to be optimistic. Engineers had crammed the platform with protections to prevent two types of piracy.

Hardware piracy means selling physical copies of PCBs (called bootlegs). By dumping the ROMs' content from a legitimate board and buying the same off-the-shelf components, pirates sold the same game for cheaper.

The CPS-1's answer was to use custom components that would not be readily available for purchase, thus preventing counterfeiters from replicating a PCB. Capcom had Ricoh exclusively fabricate the two custom ASICs, the CPS-A, and CPS-B. To protect against decapping and reverse-engineering, metal grids were layered on top of the ASICs[32].

Software piracy involved operators purchasing an authentic game to get the PCBs but then copying ROMs to get newer games for free.

Capcom's response was a two-way verification. The hardware could be actively used by the software to check the board's authenticity, backed by "passive" mechanisms that allowed the hardware to check the software behavior.

```
                         WARNING
  This game is for use in all countries
  excluding the United States of America,
  Canada, Mexico and Japan.
  Sales, export or operation inside these
  countries may be construed as copyright
  and trademark infringement and is strictly
  prohibited.
  Violators are subject to severe penalties
  and will be prosecuted to the full extent
  of the law.
```

Capcom's disclaimer when a CPS-1 game boots

2.9.1 The Ever Changing CPS-B

The heart of the protection system is the CPS-B. The core idea is to make it behave differently depending on the game it is supposed to run.

To this effect, twenty-five versions the CPS-B exist[15], sometimes differing between revision of the same game[42].

Game Name	Revision	CPS-B	Year
Forgotten Worlds		CPS-B-01	1988
Lost Worlds		CPS-B-01	1988
Ghouls'n Ghosts		CPS-B-01	1988
Strider		CPS-B-01	1989
Dynasty Wars		CPS-B-02	1989
Willow		CPS-B-03	1989
U.N Squadron		CPS-B-11	1989
Final Fight	Original	CPS-B-04	1989
Final Fight	900112	CPS-B-01	1989
Final Fight	900424	CPS-B-03	1989
Final Fight	900613	CPS-B-05	1989
1941: Counter Attack		CPS-B-05	1990
Mercs		CPS-B-12	1990
Mega Twins		CPS-B-14	1990
Magic Sword		CPS-B-13	1990
Carrier Air Wing		CPS-B-16	1990
Nemo		CPS-B-15	1990
Street Fighter II: The World Warrior	Original	CPS-B-11	1991
Street Fighter II: The World Warrior	910204	CPS-B-17	1991
Street Fighter II: The World Warrior	910318	CPS-B-05	1991
Street Fighter II: The World Warrior	910228	CPS-B-18	1991
Street Fighter II: The World Warrior	910411	CPS-B-15	1991

A selection of the many Capcom CPS-1 game revisions

In the early days of the CP-System, the CPS-B chips changed frequently. The table above only contains a few of the many PCB revisions. There is a correlation between the number of revisions and how successful a game was. Street Fighter 2 was revised 34 times, while Final Fight received 13 "refreshes".

With the release of "Three Wonders", Capcom stopped changing the CPS-B in favor of a better protection system. All CPS-B ASICs onward were CPS-B v21.

Game Name	CPS-B	Year
Three Wonders	CPS-B-21	1991
The King of Dragons	CPS-B-21	1991
Captain Commando	CPS-B-21	1991
Knights of the Round	CPS-B-21	1991
Street Fighter II: Champion Edition	CPS-B-21	1992
Adventure Quiz: Capcom World 2	CPS-B-21	1992
Varth: Operation Thunderstorm	CPS-B-21	1992
Quiz & Dragons: Capcom Quiz Game	CPS-B-21	1992
Street Fighter II' Turbo: Hyper Fighting	CPS-B-21	1992
Ken Sei Mogura: Street Fighter II	CPS-B-21	1993
Pnickies	CPS-B-21	1993
Quiz Tonosama no Yabo 2	CPS-B-21	1995
Pang! 3	CPS-B-21	1995
Mega Man the Power Battle	CPS-B-21	1995

After 1991, all CPS-1 games used CPS-B v21

2.9.2 ID Check

The simplest copy protection available is the chip ID check. By polling a register, the m68k prompts the CPS-B to return its version number. A version match lets the code know if it is running on the right PCB and resets the CPU if it isn't.

To make instructions patching of the 68000 ROMs more difficult, calls to verify the chip ID are placed in several locations in the code. Motivated programmers tried anyway[48]!

2.9.3 Multiplication Check

Starting with CPS-B v21, a slightly more robust feature gave the CPS-B the ability to perform multiplications. Two registers are written and a third can be read. The 68000 code checks that the returned multiplication result is the expected value.

2.9.4 Moving Registers

The CPS-B registers move between revisions. The offset and range do not change, but the offset of each register inside that mapping is different. Accessing the scroll control, scroll priority, and palette upload registers is done slightly differently for each game.

Additionally, the meaning of each bit field inside each register is altered between versions.

2.9.5   Unexpected Behavior Detection

Protections described so far involved active software and passive hardware. The hardware can also actively monitor the software by leveraging the moving register policy. If the CPS-B detects incoherent values written to the wrong registers, it sets and locks all palettes of all layers to black.

The game still runs in the background and the audio is played but the screen doesn't display anything. The only way to recover is to reboot the machine[29]... only for the screen to turn black again.

2.9.6   Invalid Offset Detection

Each game uses a different amount of assets for each of its SCROLL and OBJ layers. On the "B" board, PAL chips such as the `STF29` discussed earlier are hard-coded with knowledge of the amount of GFX ROM attributed to each layer.

Tile references pointing beyond a range are ignored resulting in rendering "holes" if a game ROMs are inserted in a non-matching "B" board.

> All graphics are stored together in the same ROMs.
>
> But the hardware knows which part of the ROM space is 8x8 tiles, 16x16 tiles, 16x16 spites, 32x32 tiles, and all games tested only draw tiles if their code falls in the valid range.
>
> If a tile is out of range, it is replaced by transparent pixels.
>
> — Mame cps-1 video driver

Trivia: Pull-up resistors on the board along the GFX ROM data lines detect if a pen value matches a tileID.

If no data is detected, `0xF` is automatically "inserted", resulting in a transparent value.

2.9.7 Configuration Key

Up to 1991, the behavior of a CPS-B was hard-coded in its silicon at the factory level. There was no way to alter or re-purpose them after they shipped.

It was not only expensive to have to revise the hardware circuits for each game, it was also a logistic difficulty to provision enough chips for a success and not be stuck with inventory on an unappreciated game. To solve this issue, Capcom revised the CPS-B chip one last time and made it configurable via software.

The whole behavior is encoded in a small internal 18 byte area using not ROM but RAM. To keep these bytes alive, the CPS-B v21 must be supplied with current at all times [29].

The configuration RAM was designed to survive when the cabinet was turned off thanks to a battery located on the soldering side of Board C and connected to the CPS-B. The chip was even designed to survive having no battery for a few minutes to allow battery replacement.

> **Trivia:** These batteries worked remarkably well since, thirty years later, one can find boards in working condition still using their original battery.

Suicide batteries

The infamous "suicide" nickname came from the effect of losing power. A CPS-B v21 without power lose its configuration and resets all its registers to "default" values that none of the games use. Capcom offered a battery replacement service to resurrect boards "C" which had committed seppuku but eventually discontinued it.

As the reader will have guessed, passionate fans found a way to bring these games back to life.

Phoenixing

The first method is called "phoenix"-ing. It is a tedious process which consists of dumping a game ROM and patching the m68k instructions to replace CPS-B registers accesses to use the "default values" [49].

People phoenixing CPS-1 boards have such intimate knowledge of the CP-System that they even changed the game to display a "Phoenix Edition" splash upon startup.

A phoenixed game boot splash screen

De-suiciding

Eventually, passionate people figured out the process of accessing and writing the CPS-B RAM. Boards can be brought back to life by re-uploading the proper configuration bytes which essentially de-suicides them[33].

2.10   Epilogue

From 1988 to 1995, Capcom used the CPS-1 to release more than thirty titles. These seven years saw the birth of three of Capcom's most loved franchises: Ghouls'n Ghosts, Final Fight, and Street Fighter 2.

To Capcom, the CPS-1 was a gamble that paid off hundredfold, allowing them to become a video game household name.

To players, the games were a series of beautifully crafted titles which both provided entertainment and emptied their pockets. The experience was so memorable that passionate people wrote emulators and even (in some extreme cases of obsession) books to keep these memories alive.

To counterfeiters, the CP-System was a problem. Capcom games were popular and generated a substantial amount of money. It is likely greed set in even more so once demand skyrocketed with the advent of AAA titles such as Street Fighter II.

Capcom engineers had designed security measures able to discourage attackers with a reasonable amount of determination. Perhaps the one flaw the CPS-1 can be faulted with is that it did not provision for the unprecedented level of popularity it enjoyed.

The money in the balance armed the counterfeiters with an unreasonable amount of tenacity. As players lined up to spend time and beat Street Fighter 2, so did the pirates to defeat the copy-protection systems. Eventually they were able to figure it out.

Of all the security measures, it would have been fair to assume the custom ASICs would be an impenetrable fortress. Astonishingly, CPS-A and CPS-B replicas were manufactured under the name "COMCO" [30]. It is unknown if an insider leaked the schematics or if someone made it their life mission to reverse-engineer these chips to make it happen but it did.

As cracks appeared in its shield, Capcom did not give up on protecting its titles. As it had proved itself able to evolve and compete in the business of producing games, it embraced the challenge of embarking on an encryption crusade against bootleggers.

2.10.1 CPS-1.5 Kabuki

In 1992, Capcom released the CP System Dash (a.k.a CPS-1.5). Fully encased in a gray plastic box, it introduced a fourth satellite "Qboard" PCB to handle playback of positional three-dimensional Qsound audio. Five games were produced until late 1993.

Game Name	Type	GFX	Year
Cadillacs and Dinosaurs	■	4 MiB	1992
Warriors of Fate	■	4 MiB	1992
The Punisher	■	4 MiB	1993
Saturday Night Slam Masters	■	6 MiB	1993
Muscle Bomber Duo: Ultimate Team Battle	■	6 MiB	1993

CPS-1.5 games: ■ Other, ■ Platform, □ Shmup, ■ Brawl, ■ Duel

The CPS 1.5 is noteworthy for its improved copy-protection. Audio instructions are stored encrypted in the ROM. The audio CPU is a special z80 dubbed Kabuki[31] able to decrypt instructions on the fly.

The encryption scheme is symmetric. A secret key is used to encrypt the ROM when it is built, and the same secret key must be used to decrypt it at runtime.

The key is not burned in the z80's silicon but, like the CPS-B v21 configuration, stored in an internal RAM. To keep that key alive, the unused pin 28 we saw on page 55 is re-purposed from "DRAM refresh" to providing power. Like the CPS-B and its RAM configuration, the z80 requires power at all times which means the system was provided with a second "suicide battery".

> **Trivia:** The protection provided by Kabuki held remarkably well over the years. It was only broken in the early 2000s[17].

2.10.2   CPS-2

With significantly improved capabilities thanks to its increased ROM capacity and higher processor clocks, the CPS-2 instantly became a smash-hit, in particular thanks to the Street Fighter Alpha series.

From 1993 to 2003, forty-two games were published. The first one was the wildly successful "Super Street Fighter II" while the last one "Hyper Street Fighter II: The Anniversary Edition" paid homage to a series that defined the platform.

In terms of copy-protection, Capcom once again cranked up security. Even though it dropped usage of Kabuki in favor of a plain z80, the platform gained encryption of its game logic.

Thanks to a custom CPU, ABI compatible with the 68000, instructions are stored encrypted in ROM and decrypted on the fly. Like Kabuki, the scheme uses a shared secret key stored in a battery-powered RAM.

The graphic asset stored in the GFXROM were slightly obfuscated. However no encryption occurred, data was only shuffled.

A strong protection

No bootlegs of CPS-2 titles are known to have ever been produced. Efforts to shed light on the CPS-2 internals started in 2000[36] via the "CPS-2 Shock Group".

Game Name	Type	GFX	Year
Super Street Fighter II: The New Challengers	■	12 MiB	1993
Eco Fighters	□	12 MiB	1993
Dungeons & Dragons: Tower of Doom	▨	12 MiB	1994
Super Street Fighter II Turbo	■	12 MiB	1994
Alien vs. Predator	▨	16 MiB	1994
Darkstalkers: The Night Warriors	■	20 MiB	1994
Ring of Destruction: Slammasters II	■	18 MiB	1994
Armored Warriors	▨	20 MiB	1994
X-Men: Children of the Atom	■	32 MiB	1994
Night Warriors: Darkstalkers' Revenge	■	32 MiB	1995
Cyberbots: Full Metal Madness	■	32 MiB	1995
Street Fighter Alpha	■	16 MiB	1995
Mega Man: The Power Battle	▨	16 MiB	1995
Marvel Super Heroes	■	32 MiB	1995
19XX: The War Against Destiny	□	16 MiB	1995
Dungeons & Dragons: Shadow over Mystara	▨	24 MiB	1996
Street Fighter Alpha 2	■	20 MiB	1996
Super Puzzle Fighter II Turbo	▨	12 MiB	1996
Mega Man 2: The Power Fighters	▨	16 MiB	1996
Street Fighter Alpha 2 Gold	■	20 MiB	1996
Quiz Nanairo Dreams: Nijiirochō no Kiseki	▨	16 MiB	1996
X-Men vs. Street Fighter	■	32 MiB	1996
Battle Circuit	▨	16 MiB	1997
Darkstalkers 3	■	32 MiB	1997
Marvel Super Heroes vs. Street Fighter	■	32 MiB	1997
Capcom Sports Club	▨	16 MiB	1997
Super Gem Fighter Mini Mix	■	20 MiB	1997
Vampire Hunter 2: Darkstalkers' Revenge	■	32 MiB	1997
Vampire Savior 2: The Lord of Vampire	■	32 MiB	1997
Marvel vs. Capcom: Clash of Super Heroes	■	32 MiB	1998
Street Fighter Alpha 3	■	32 MiB	1998
Giga Wing	□	16 MiB	1999
Jyangokushi: Haō no Saihai	▨	16 MiB	1999
Dimahoo	□	16 MiB	2000
Mars Matrix: Hyper Solid Shooting	□	32 MiB	2000
1944: The Loop Master	□	32 MiB	2000
Mighty! Pang	▨	8 MiB	2000
Progear	□	16 MiB	2001
Puzz Loop 2	▨	16 MiB	2001
Janpai Puzzle Choko	▨	16 MiB	2001
Hyper Street Fighter II: The Anniversary Edition	▨	32 MiB	2003

The protection system was remarkably strong and held for nearly 14 years. The scheme is so interesting it deserves its own book. Here are a few fun facts to open your appetite.

1. Only the ROM read accesses are decrypted by the custom 68000. Read and write operations to the RAM are kept in "clear".

2. The early "CPS-2 Shock Group" effort managed to inject instructions in a running game and have them executed[37]. That was enough to allow unencrypted ROM extraction. This breakthrough opened the door to CPS-2 emulation. The method was convoluted but it worked. Emulators had to ship with a per-game XOR image to "decrypt" the 68000 ROMs.

3. The encryption scheme was completely reverse engineered in 2007 by Mame programmers. It turned out the secret encryption keys were not randomly generated[38]. Capcom used linearly increasing sequences of numbers (1,2,3,4,...) or permutations of the same sequence.

4. Every ten seconds the custom 68000 must receive a watchdog command on its `D1` register. If it doesn't, it stops decrypting the ROM instructions. They look as follows.

```
cmpi.l  #$19660419,D1   ; Dungeons & Dragons
cmpi.l  #$19720121,D1   ; Marvel vs Capcom
cmpi.l  #$19721027,D1   ; Giga Wing
cmpi.l  #$19720327,D1   ; X-Men Vs. Street Fighter
...
```

As you will probably have noticed, these values have the pattern of birthday dates!

Previous table, CPS-2 games: ■ Other, ■ Platform, □ Shmup, ■ Brawl, ■ Duel.

Software Concepts

Nothing tells you more about a system than the process of actually building software for it.

The rest of this book describes a full game production pipeline. The goal is to deepen the understanding of Capcom's platform by not only writing code and generating assets but also learning how to process them in order to generate ROMs.

This chapter describes the high-level architecture. It is intentionally light on details since those are provided in subsequent chapters.

The pipeline we will describe ingests the source code (`.s`/`.c`) written by programmers, the samples (`.wav`) and music (`.vgm`) from the musicians, and the graphics assets (`.png`) produced by the artists. The outputs are four sets of ROMs ready to be burned on EPROMs.

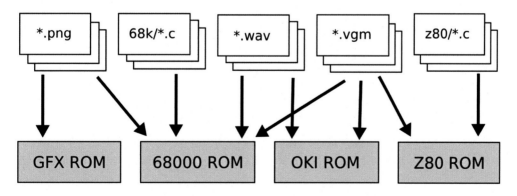

Game ROM dependency graph

Some dependencies in the graph are simple to the extreme. The z80 source code (`.c` and `.s`) only impacts the z80 ROM. Likewise, the m68k code (also `.c` and `.s`) ends up in the 68000 ROM.

Other dependencies are more convoluted. The `.wav` sample files for example need to be compressed to ADPCM before being added to the OKI ROM. To be referenceable at runtime, each sample is given an integer ID. These IDs must be collected into a `.h` header and this file must be compiled along with the rest of the 68000 code.

Likewise, the `.png` files containing artwork are transformed to indexed format before making their way to the GFX ROM. They also require generating a `.h` header file, this time containing tileID. Additionally, a `.c` file containing each tile palette is generated in order to be compiled into the 68000 ROM.

An even more complicated graph emerges from the music `.vgm` files. The music track contains YM2151 commands that must be transformed in bytecode, stored in a `.c` file, and compiled along with the z80 code. To be referenced, a header file containing music ID must also be generated and compiled with the 68000 ROM. Music is also embellished with audio samples which must also be compressed to ADPCM and added to the OKI ROM.

To complicate things even further, each of the four ROM mentioned must use different `WORD` size and interleaving across the chips containing it.

3.1 CCPS: The CPS-1 Build System

As this book was being written, several tools were authored to validate the understanding of the hardware.

Ultimately these tools were combined into a build system called `ccps`. The rest of this book occasionally refers to `ccps` but tries to keep the abstraction level high so readers can build their own build system if they desire.

Even if only to check what obscure compiler flags must be used, it is freely available, open source, and a few command lines away. It also welcomes pull requests :P !

```
$ git clone https://github.com/fabiensanglard/ccps.git
$ cd ccps
$ ./makeAndBuild.sh
$ ccps ...
```

3.2 Programming Language

For all their CPS-1 titles, Capcom developers used z80/m68k assembly. They did not have much choice since high-level languages did not allow variable placement and humans were better at hand optimizing instructions. Additionally, ROM space was precious and controlling the volume of instructions with accuracy was paramount.

Even with improvements in modern compiler capabilities, output compactness, and optimization performances, a developer willing to take a CPS-1 to the next level will undoubtedly use assembly.

Since the goal of this book is to explain how things work, it uses C for its greater readability and wider knowledge base among programmers. A little bit of assembly is used but only to bootstrap the CPUs.

3.3 CPUs Bootstrapping

Without libraries, frameworks, dynamic linker, syscalls, virtual memory, a loader, or even an operating system, CP-System games run on the bare metal.

Bootstrapping involves simple things like setting the stack pointer and the instruction pointer of a CPU. But it also involves harder tasks like setting up interrupts and more importantly preparing the program to run before calling its `main` function.

An innocent six line C program offers a glimpse into what is involved.

```
char a;
char b = 0;
const int c = 1;
const char* d = "bar";
char e = 5;
int f(){...}
```

After compilation and linking, this program will result into a binary blob of raw instructions (no container like ELF or PE) `prog.rom`. Burned on a ROM, it is mapped somewhere in the CPU address space depending on the mapping established for the z80 and m68k.

During the linking stage, all the variables and functions are given an address in either ROM or RAM.

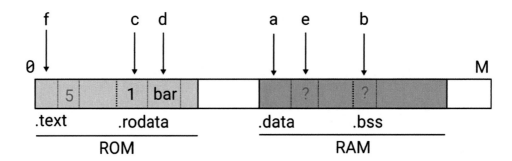

CPU Memory address space, ROM and RAM

Read-only

Instructions for `f` go in section `.text` at offset 0. Since the linker knows both where the ROM will be mapped and the section offset in the ROM, it can inline calls to `.text + 0`. This means `0x0000` for both the z80 and the m68k.

Const values `c` and `d` are read only so they go in ROM as well. These are grouped in section `.rodata` apart from `.text`. Access to these two symbols are respectively inlined with values `.rodata + 0` and `.rodata + 1`.

Read-Write

Symbol `a` is interesting because it is readable but also writable. The linker will have assigned a RAM address (starting at `0xD000` on z80 and `0xFF0000` on m68k). Since it is uninitialized, it will point to whatever is in the RAM when it started.

Like `a`, `b` is readable and writable but it is initialized to value `0`. The linker can make `a` point to RAM and even group zero-initialized variables together in `.bss` but setting the value to 0 cannot be done. This is something the bootstrap will have to resolve.

Finally we come to variable `e`. Since it is writable, the linker will have used the next available address in RAM after `a`. But how can the linker initialize that location to value `5` since it can only write to file `pro.rom` which is not mapped there?

The answer is that it cannot. That task, called "copy-down", is another thing the bootstrap will have to take care of.

Since they involve low-level operations, both bootstraps for z80 and the m68k are written using assembly and bundled in a file named `crt0.s`.

3.4   Systems Communication

There are many chips in the machine that need to talk to each other. In the hierarchy we studied in the first chapter, each line is an interface.

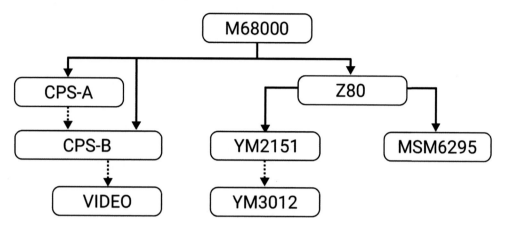

That is a total of eight communication lines, but the dotted ones in the drawing are not programmable, lowering the task to understanding five APIs.

3.4.1   m68k → CPSA and m68k → CPS-B

Communication occurs over the CPS-A and CPS-B registers. Additional draw commands are written by the 68000 to the GFXRAM where they are read by the CPS-A. All access to GFXRAM is arbitrated by the m68k bus protocol.

3.4.2   z80 → YM2151

Communication occurs over the YM2151 registers which are mapped on the z80 bus. This access is arbitrated by the z80 bus protocol.

3.4.3   z80 → MSM6295

Communication occurs over the MSM6295 registers which are mapped on the z80 bus. This access is arbitrated by the z80 bus protocol.

3.4.4 m68k → z80

Communication between these two CPUs is not trivial. They both have their own bus protocol, run at different speeds, have different address spaces, and data widths.

Try to think of a design yourself with the following constraints. There are two 1 byte latches. On one side is a m68k running at 10MHz which can write in them but not read. On the other end is a z80, working at 3.579 MHz which can read but not write them.

How can you make these two CPUs talk to each other reliably, making sure the stream of commands features no duplicates and no drops?

3.4.5 Interrupts

Both the z80 and the m68k have interrupt systems. These are used to solve many problems and in particular the issue of communicating over the latches.

Since the reader (z80) runs slower than the writer (m68k) it is possible for a latch value to be overwritten (write twice) before it is read.

Inverting the ratio is done precisely via interrupts. The m68k's IPL1 line is directly connected to the VSYNC line of the video system. Likewise, the z80 INT line is connected to the timer (CT1) line of the YM2151.

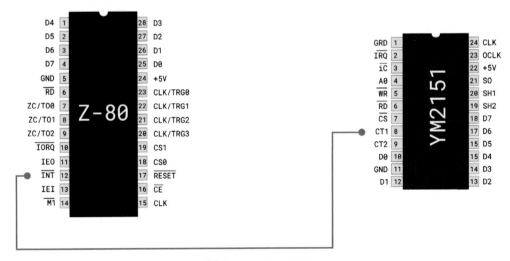

z80 interrupt system

This configuration lets the writer tick every 16ms while the reader ticks every 4ms. This ensures no latch value can be dropped but introduces the problem of duplicate reads.

To avoid these, the z80 commits to disregard a latch content if its content did not change since the last time it was checked.

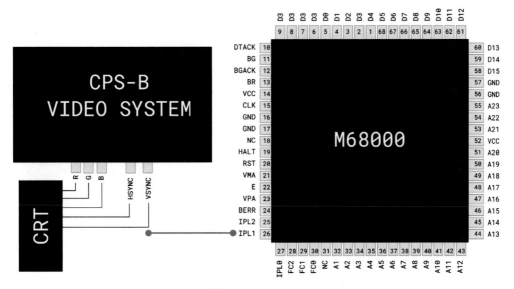

m68k interrupt system

This introduces an ultimate problem. It is not possible for the m68k CPU to send the same byte twice in a row. To work around this, the writer commits on never writing the same byte twice which is done via a no-op byte (0xFF) written after every byte.

3.4.6   Back in the days

The system and conventions we just described allows for reliable data exchange but it does not give a semantic to the values in the latches.

A developer is free to give any meaning to the latches since they control both the writer and the reader. Maybe you can even take a second to think how you would design this interface if you had to before we study how Capcom did it.

In a game like Street Fighter II, developers took the approach of not giving values an "immediate" meaning. Communication is a stream of bytes which must be reconstructed on the receiving end before being interpreted.

When interrupted, the z80 reads the byte in latch 1 and appends it into a circular buffer.

Interpretation happens in the "main" thread. A byte value `FE` means that the next byte is the ID of a music that should start playback.

Otherwise the value is a sound ID to be played immediately on the OKI. This scheme wastes a single byte value to overhead. It allows for 256 music IDs and 254 samples IDs.

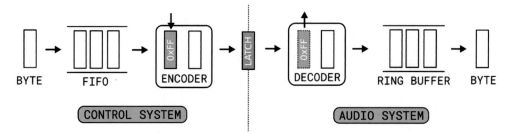

BYTE   FIFO   ENCODER   DECODER   RING BUFFER   BYTE

CONTROL SYSTEM   AUDIO SYSTEM

Street Fighter comm model. Stream encoding via `0xFF`

Notice how the encoder, on the m68k side, injects `0xFF` no-op bytes after each write to the latch and how the decoder ignores them.

What about the other latch? Street Fighter II only ever uses the first one. The other one is left unused.

No sound driver can rule them all

Given the capabilities of the communication system described above, it would be fair to assume all Capcom games used it. That would be wrong.

The "sound driver" kept on evolving, sometimes changing drastically even between two games made consecutively by the same team.

In Final Fight, a sound ID received for playback is directly forwarded to the OKI. In Street Fighter II, a translation table is used. The ID received is an index into an array containing the actual OKI ID along with the channel and volume to use.

The merits of a translation table may be explained by the size of Capcom team and the inability to do a "full build" easily at the time.

If the sound team had to change the OKI layout, all IDS used by the m68k would be invalid. With a translation table, the sound team was able to make any change they wanted and keep their sound and music IDs backward compatible.

3.4.7   Our sound driver

The sound driver described in the next pages uses the same architecture as Capcom. It relies on interrupts on both sides. Besides being used for the latch communication, the interrupts also maintain a counter to pace the main threads.

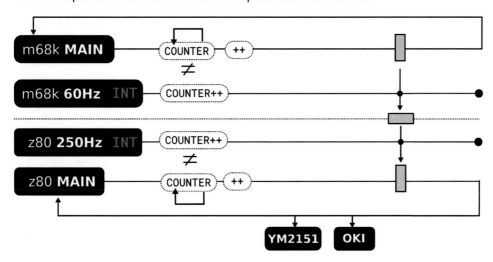

The communication protocol however is not streamed. Whereas it is more powerful, it is also much more complicated. For simplicity, a byte is immediately interpreted without the need to rebuild a stream.

The byte space is divided in two. If the MSB is set to one (0x80) it is a request for sound effect playback and if the MSB is set to zero 0x00 it indicates a music playback.

This leaves "only" 126 sound values and 127 music values but is more than enough for the intended purpose. Volume is hard-coded and round-robin rotation is used to pick between channels 1 or 2 to serve a request.

3.5   Tracking Wall-time

The wall-time is the time experienced by players. Both CPUs must be able to measure it. The m68k must do so in order to sample inputs and run the game engine at the intended speed. The z80 is under the same constraint for the music where it must keep track of pauses and note duration.

Modern systems have Real Time Clock (RTC) chips to do this but the CP-System is devoid of it. The solution is to leverage the counters which are incremented each time the main thread is interrupted. Depending on the CPU these accumulators will have different granularity.

The m68k tracks time in units of 16ms while the z80 can do the same in increments of 4ms.

3.6 Randomness

Pseudo-random series of numbers can be achieved using Maximum-Length LFSRs (Linear Feedback Shift Register). On the m68k, a 32-bit registers will give 4,194,304 different values before repeating itself. On the z80, the 8-bit register will only provide 256 values.

The only tricky part is to pick a seed to initialize the register. Street Fighter 2 uses the frame counter while other titles read the content of the CPU register during bootstrap. The latter method does not work well when working with emulators (they usually initialize their registers to zero) and should be avoided.

3.7 Banking System

This part applies only to the z80 which uses an infamous banking system. The constraint is to make sure the window mapped at [0xB000– 0xBFFF] is slid to "see" the proper part of the ROM.

This is done via the Bank Switch control register mapped at 0xF004 . The value written is multiplied by 0x4000 which gives the starting offset (in ROM space) of the sliding window. Writing 0 makes 0xB000 in z80 space map to 0x0000 in ROM space, writing 0x0001 makes 0xB000 in z80 space map to 0x4000 in ROM space, and writing 0x0002 makes 0xB000 in z80 space map to 0xB000 in ROM space.

This adjustment must be performed before accessing any address falling within the banking interval.

GFX System

Since the graphic pipeline of the CPS-1 is hard-coded in the silicon of the CPS-A and CPS-B, there is no code to write and nothing to compile.

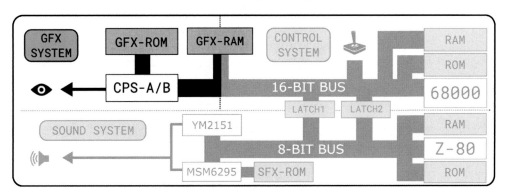

The GFX System components

It sounds simple but there is more at hand than converting graphic assets to GFXROM format. Even though all types of assets use the same pixel format, observant readers will have noticed that palettes are not stored in GFXROM. Special care must be taken to save them and provide them to the m68k later, along with a way to reference them.

The other constraints to consider are the "hard-coded regions" of the GFXROM where OBJ, STAR1, STAR2, SCR1, SCR2, and SCR3 assets must reside. If a tile is not where it should be, a draw command is simply ignored.

All boards use a different layout. The Street Fighter II board and its STF29 PAL slice the 6MiB GFXROM in four areas (OBJ, SCR1, SCR2, and SCR3) .

A board running Final Fight uses a S224B PAL which carves the space in the same four area types but with different offset and proportions over a smaller 2MiB space.

The PAL found on Forgotten Worlds' board, the `LW621`, is more complex as it divides the GFXROM in five areas to also include interleaved STAR1 and STAR2 bytecode.

4.1 Tile Format

All tiles are stored continuously in memory, using groups of four bytes encoding eight pens. Rows of pens are stored one after another. The dimension of a tile varies depending on the layers. OBJ and SCR2 use the same 16x16 tiles which mean their tiles are 16*16 / 2 = 128 bytes. For the fine tuned SCR1, which uses 8x8, each tile uses 32 bytes. Finally the larger SCR3 uses 512 bytes for each of its 32x32 tiles.

4.2 GFX Layout

The EPROMs are organized in groups of four chips and serialized. On a board like Street Fighter II, we find three groups of four. Inside each group, chips are interleaved every WORD (two bytes).

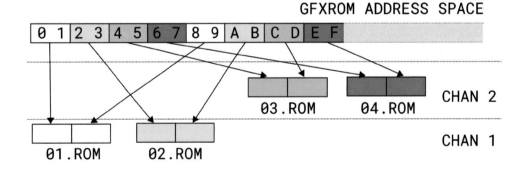

4.3 Channels

The channels mentioned earlier are now visible. ROM 01 and ROM 02 are paired on channel 1 to provide 32-bit data. Likewise, ROM 03 and 04 are paired on channel 2. The same division is applied to the rest of the ROMs with the same principle.

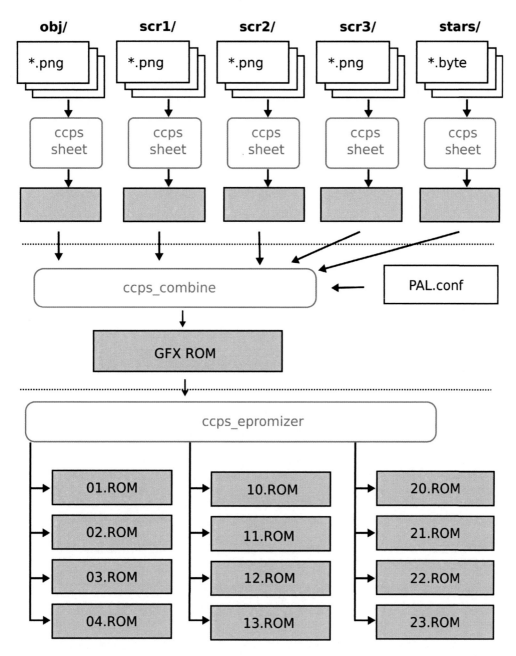

The Street Fighter II board build generates twelve ROMs. Each group stores 2 MiB. Group [1-4] starts at 0x000000, group [10-13] at 0x200000, and ROMs [20-23] at 0x400000. Each chip goes in the matching numbered DIP slot (see page 42).

4.4 Back in the Days

The artwork was the part of a game that required the most people. On a big title such as Street Fighter II, that task kept twenty artists busy, out of a team of forty.

Producing tilemap (background) assets for the SCROLL layers was junior artists' responsibility. It required little supervision since the artwork had to be rectangular and the visual importance was not the highest.

Producing assets for the OBJ layer, on the other hand, was much more elaborate. Four steps were involved: outline drawing, allocation, detailed drawing, and finally dotting.

4.4.1 Pen and Papers

The artistic direction was established by the planner of the game. Their goal was to produce concept art and pose outlines in order to capture the essence of a character, as well as establishing proportions and movements. After that, senior artists took over for fine tuning.

> When I joined on Street Fighter II, Akiman had already done the rough drafts.
>
> There were four of us as character leads - Satoru Yamashita , Yoshiaki Ohji, and Ikuo Nakayama in addition to myself. Satoru was the most skilled, so he would take Ryu and Ken.
>
> One day, Akiman brought us the rough sketches of a pro wrestler, sumo wrestler, and a beast, and said "decide who does what." To be fair, we played paper-rock-scissors to determine!
>
> — Eri Nakamura[22]

Even though it was not the norm, it could happen that the planner took care of every aspect of a character (especially if the topic was dear to their heart).

> I created all Chun-Li's graphics in just 1 month.
>
> — Akiman[44]

However, "Chun-Li" stories seem to have been rare occurrences. In the case of Final Fight, Satoru Yamashita animated Guy and Haggar but Akiman drew the key animations for both of them.

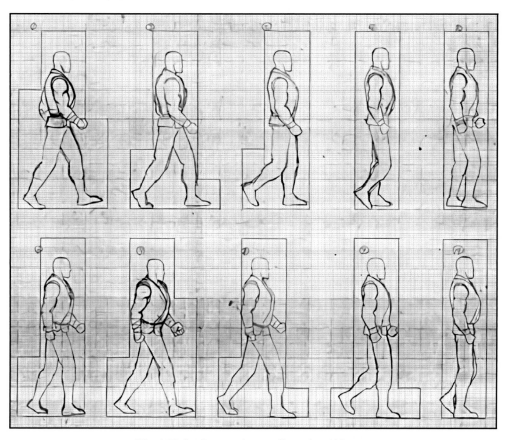

Final Fight Guy sprite outlines by Akiman

4.4.2 Non-square Grid Paper

To draw both outlines and detailed versions of the sprites, artists used a special paper with a double grid system.

There was a "light" grid which used non-square proportions to match the CP-system video aspect ratio of 10:7. Artists were able to draw normally without having to worry about distortion since rectangle elements would match the CPS-1's stretched pixels.

The paper featured a second "darker" grid which grouped elements 16 by 16 to match the OBJ tile dimension. This was an essential feature for the allocation step.

4.4.3 OBJ Allocation

If breaking free of the rectangular sprites was a blessing for the artists, it was a problem for Capcom project managers. In an era where ROM chips were very expensive, a game was allocated a ROM budget at its beginning which it could not be exceeded.

Before the CPS-1, remaining within the budget was a simple matter of a division. The number of sprites allowed to the art team was ROM size / rectangular sprite size. But the free form factor introduced a tracking problem.

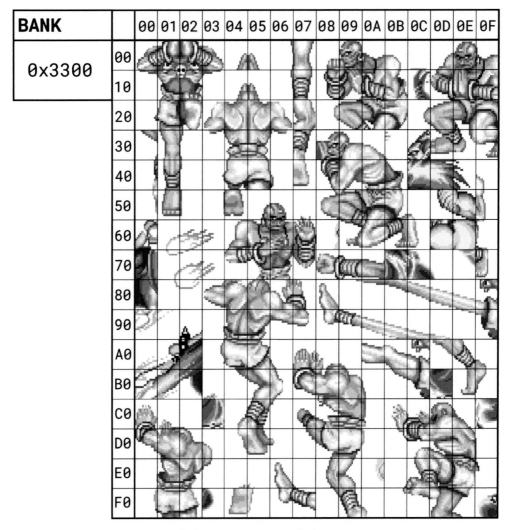

Dhalsim reconstructed sheet

The solution to the allocation problem came with paper and scissors.

> In order to make the best use of the capacity we had, we wrote the ROM's capacity on a board, and cut and paste the pixel characters on the board. If there was space left on the board, then there was open capacity in the ROM. So, from there we started filling in the spaces, like a puzzle.
>
> We saved making the ending for last, and by the time we got there we were all out of capacity. We were wondering what to do, when we found a board that had gone missing under a desk.
>
> We called it the "Mirac-ulous Memory."
>
> — Nin [22]

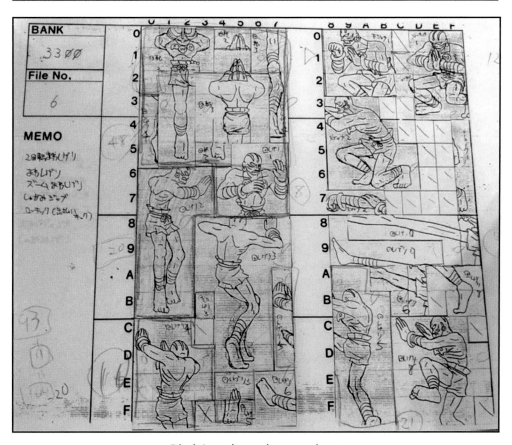

Dhalsim released paper sheet

Only two of these sheets have ever been released, one mostly featuring Dhalsim[21] and another one called the "Ryu sheet"[54]. Thanks to the imprint left in the GFXROM and the knowledge of the pixel format/layout, all other spreadsheets can be reconstructed.

For a game like Street Fighter II, a budget of 6MiB GFX was approved. With 4.6 MiB dedicated to sprites, 144 OBJ sheets were printed. That was a lot at the time and only warranted because the team had managed to score a huge hit with Final Fight on a tiny 2MiB budget[44].

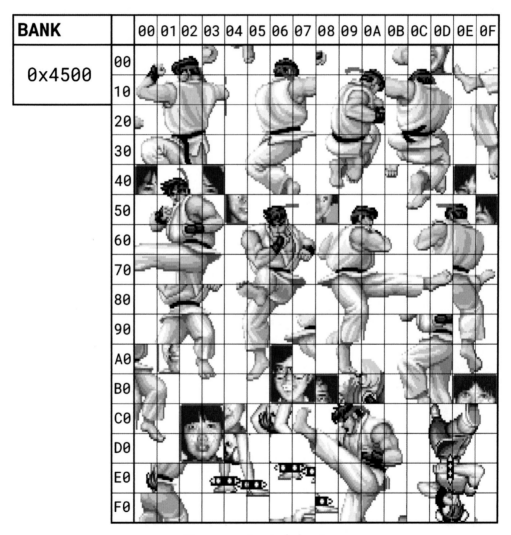

Ryu reconstructed sheet

Comparing the released material with what actually shipped is the source of many discoveries and hypotheses.

The Dhalsim sheet sits at offset `0x3300` in the GFXROM. It is a near perfect match with the paper version except for the portion starting at `0x60`. One of the poses was dropped in favor of the Chun-Li animation "Hundred Rending Legs" which would indicate it was a later addition.

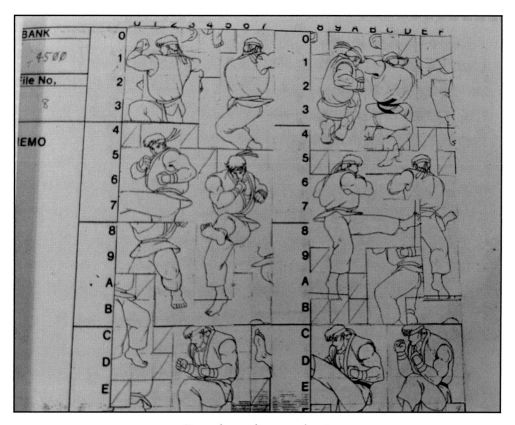

Ryu released paper sheet

Ryu's sheet `0x4500` allows us to guess even more about the production process. Large coherent sprites show that at the beginning of the production process multiple sheets were allocated on a per-character basis. Tiles were layed out and kept together as much as possible to facilitate visual inspection.

As the project progressed, the team scraped the bottom of the barrel and started to allocate space on a per-tile basis. They sometimes spread a character pose across multiple sheets, like in Dhalsim's sheet where portions of Blanka can be found.

4.4.4 The Sheet System

Besides sparsely describing it, Capcom employees never elaborated on the sheet system. For which title and for how long it was used in total are questions that were never answered.

Thanks to an understanding of the GFXROM format, it is possible to peek back in time. The digital structure is an imprint of what the paper sheet looked like. These reconstructed sheets can provide answers.

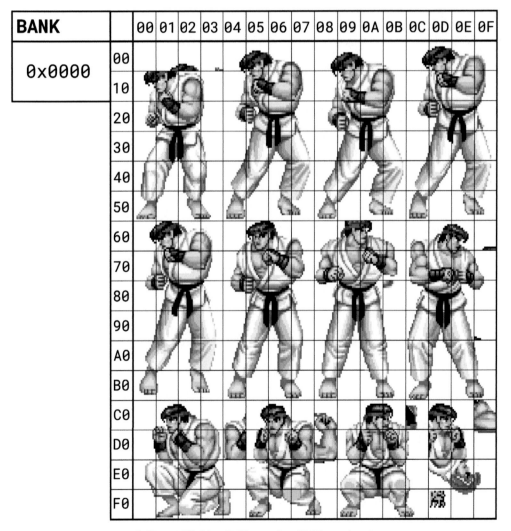

A Street Fighter II Champion Edition sheet

Examining the GFXROM structure of all games published on CPS-1 uniformly reveals tiles grouped to match actual drawings, which implies usage of paper and scissors.

The GFXROM layout started to change with the first title using the CPS-2. In Super Street Fighter II, the sheets of the twelve legacy contestants are the same as the ones used in Street Fighter II Champion Edition. However, new character sheets look like they were created with an automated allocator which sliced sprites vertically.

Inspection of subsequent games' GFXROM indicate that all games released on CPS-2 used an automated OBJ allocator.

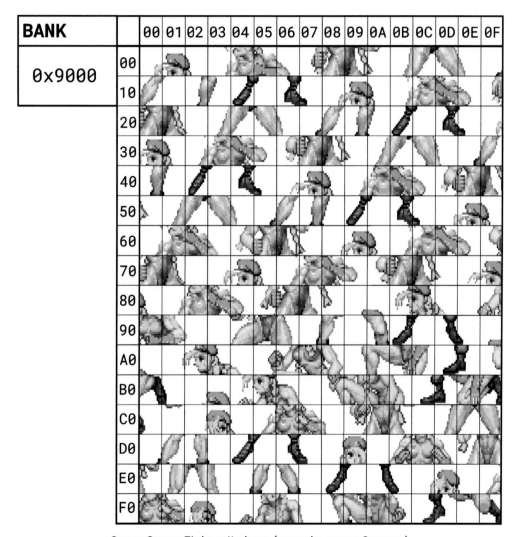

Super Street Fighter II sheet (new character Cammy)

SONY MICRO COMPUTER
SMC-70
ソニーマイクロコンピューター ¥228,000
SONY
16色表示グラフィック重視設計、コマンド拡張機能付Sony BASIC
搭載。高速CP/M*対応、最大768KB、16ビットマシンへも拡張可能。
SONY
SONY

4.4.5   Digitizing Art

To digitize their drawings, Capcom employees used SMC-70 computers. Manufactured by Sony, the SMC-70 hit both the US and Japan market in the end of 1982. What is particularly noteworthy about this machine is that it is built around extensibility.

The main element of a SMC-70 features its keyboard along with the core parts such as the z80 running at 4MHz, 64KiB RAM, and 64 KiB of VRAM. The rest is entirely configurable via daisy chained extenders.

The only limit to the chain system is the capacity of the power supply, which must be located at the very back of the chain.

This architecture allowed Sony's machine capabilities to range from simple office work to a powerful video editing tool in its most extensive chaining configuration.

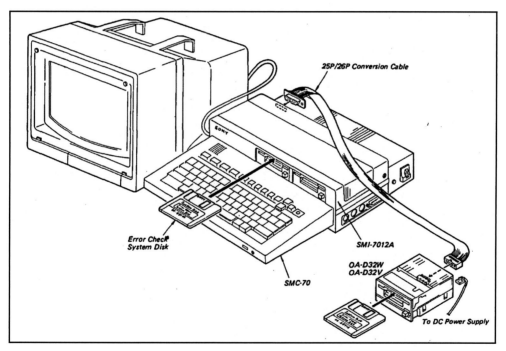

A SMC-70 extended with a SMI-7012. Power supply at the very back

Sony, the big iron

On one hand, the substantial list of extensions and peripherals, totaling nearly 40 pieces all made by Sony, is a testament to the company's commitment. On the other hand, it also embodies a desire to remain in control of the platform by keeping other manufacturers from contributing to the eco-system.

Extension Name	Peripheral Name	Function
SMI-7011		3.5" floppy drive bay (internal with 1 drive)
SMI-7012		3.5" floppy drive bay (internal with 2 drives)
SMI-7013		3.5" floppy drive bay (external with 1 drive)
SMI-7014		3.5" floppy drive bay (external with 2 drives)
SMI-7016		Floppy Disk Control Unit
	SMI-7020	Dot Matrix Printer
SMI-7031		RS232C Serial Interface
SMI-7032		IEEE-488 Interface Unit
SMI-7050		Cache Disk Unit
SMI-7056		Supercharger: 5MHz i8086 w/ 256 KiB RAM.
	SMI-7060	10-Key Numeric Key Pad
SMI-7070		Video Signal Converter
SMI-7073		RGB Superimposer
SMI-7074		NTSC Superimposer
SMI-7075		Videotizer
SMI-7080		Battery Back-up Unit

SMC-70 extensions and peripherals [63]

Noteworthy capabilities

The SMC-70 is notable for being the first computer to allow a 3.5" floppy reader (also invented by Sony in 1981) and its ability to display kanji characters via a ROM extension.

However, it is really when it comes to graphic capabilities that the machine stood out. Four resolutions were available, ranging from low-resolution 320x200 using sixteen colors up to high-resolution 640x200 in two colors.

The 16 colors mode was particularly interesting to Capcom artists since it was a perfect match to the CPS-1 pen system.

4.4.6　Tiny Character Editor

The SMC-70 had no ability to use a scanner. The digitization process was entirely achieved by hand. To help them in their task, artists used a tool called TCE (Tiny Character Editor). Although no screenshot ever emerged, Capcom employees gave a rough description of its minimalist approach.

> You had a 16 pixel grid, a 16-color palette, and that was it.
>
> — Koichi Yotsui (Strider planner)

4.4.7 Dotting

For both SCROLL and OBJ elements, dotting was done on a tile basis. The artist's task was to look at their detailed graph paper drawing and decide, for each rectangular element in the tile, which color of the palette to use for it.

Pixel-art was a tedious and repetitive process which required a sense of aesthetic creativity to deal with the cases where a line crossed a pixel. Drop the pixel, include it plain, or attempt to anti-alias with a color in the palette were difficult choices to make.

No mouse was available. Out of the box options were either a keyboard or a keypad. Some employees, satisfied with neither, built themselves a custom joystick.

A SMC-70 with a keypad. A likely dotter setup

At the very least, employees were free to use what was the most effective to them.

> I used a keyboard to draw all the graphics for Vampire and Street Fighter 2.
>
> — Akiman[11]

> As everything was in hexadecimal we used the 0-F keys and the arrows to make the sprites.
>
> There was this one guy who made a complete racket mashing away on his keyboard. He used to do overtime and didn't even sleep, so we'd all have no choice but to stay awake and keep working as well.
>
> — Akiman[24]

4.4.8 Saving Tiles

Artists attempted to reuse tiles as much as possible to reduce usage of the scarce ROM space available. In Street Fighter 2, there was only enough GFXROM for eleven challengers. Ken is a patchwork and a palette swap on top of Ryu tiles base. It "weighs" only 98,304 bytes. A remarkable achievement compared to characters such as Zangief (622,592 bytes), Honda (491,520 bytes), or Ryu (442,368 bytes).

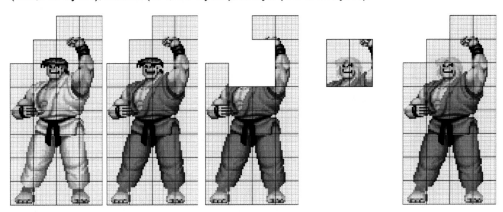

Made with 2MiB GFXROM, Final Fight is even more impressive with 21 enemies and 6 bosses. The minions are made of seven bases, diversified with patches and palettes.

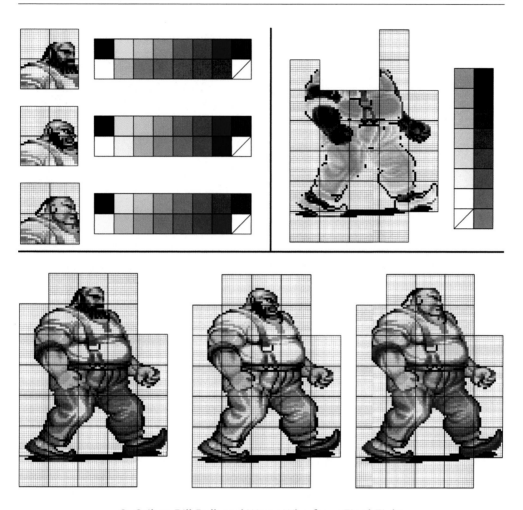

G. Oriber, Bill Bull, and Wong Who from Final Fight

Everyone on the development thought Final Fight was going to be allocated with a large memory capacity, but we were wrong. That's why the final boss Belger hops around like that: we didn't have enough memory to add more graphics for a walking pattern.

However, making something cool with limited resources is like a puzzle to me, so I thought it was fun.

— Nin[64]

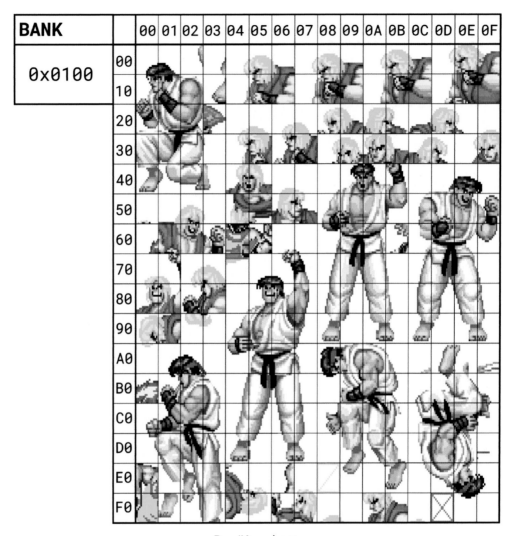

Ryu/Ken sheet

Ryu and Ken use the same seven first colors of their palette to facilitate the patching process.

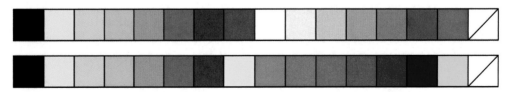

BANK		00	01	02	03	04	05	06	07	08	09	0A	0B	0C	0D	0E	0F
0x4e00	00																
	10																

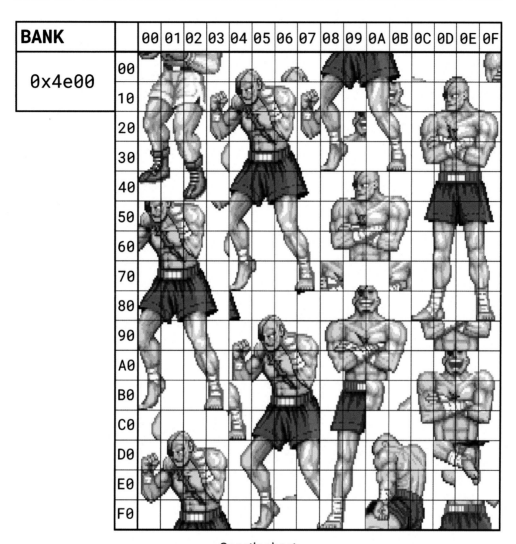

Sagat's sheet

Sagat's laughing animation is double optimized. The sequence is made of two poses where only the bust is replaced while the legs remain the same. Moreover, the left leg is missing. It is reconstructed at runtime using an horizontal mirror of the right leg found at `0xB9`.

> **Trivia:** The capacity of the ASICs to flip tiles horizontally was used extensively in Street Fighter II when challengers faced left or right. Not really an issue for symmetrical characters, except for Sagat's eye patch switches sides when he turns.

4.4.9 Team Structure and Culture

The art team had a strong hierarchy based on skills and seniority.

> Planners at the top.
> Senior artists get to work on sprites.
> Junior artists work on backgrounds.
>
> — Akiman [55]

The structure was flat with no involvement of intermediate managers. Out of the twenty people doing artwork on Street Fighter II, all of them reported to a single person, Akiman [45].

As layered as they were, operations were not set in stone and employees could climb the ladder quickly. Akiman was hired on "Dyn Side Arms" in 1986 as a SCROLL artist, the bottom of the artist ladder. Two years later, he was a Planner on Forgotten Worlds and went on to work on Final Fight and Street Fighter 2 in the same capacity.

Work Ethic

A strong working culture was established from the very top.

> We had vacation days, but Yoshiki Okamoto (Capcom development leader) would get mad if you took the day off. A lot of people got yelled at by him for that, "Hey, why weren't you here on Sunday?!"
>
> I don't think anyone can beat my record for "percentage of time lived at Capcom." During game developments, I always slept under my desk.
>
> I had a whole futon laid out and everything! When things were really busy, Yoshiki Okamoto would be setting new deadlines every 10 hours, so I couldn't leave my computer… that's how I acquired the habit of sleeping under my desk.
>
> By the way, even now that I'm freelance, I still sleep under my computer desk at home.
>
> — Akiman [55]

Poaching

Retaining talent was a top priority. The credit screen of Street Fighter II illustrates Capcom's cautiousness. Artists were only credited by their nicknames.

Street Fighter II credit screen does not use actual names for fear of poaching

Trivia: The most recognition available was a specialty next to a nickname. Some "credit screens" like in "Dynasty Wars" feature **OBJ** artists and **SCR** artists.

Despite its precautions, Capcom lost numerous employees over the years. Among them was Takashi Nishiyama who made Street Fighter 1 and then went on to direct "Fatal Fury: The King Of Fighters" for Capcom's arch-rival, SNK[56].

4.4.10   Inspiration

For Street Fighter II, artists' inspiration came from various outlets.

Mangas such as "Yasunori Katō" helped to give birth to Dictator while Tao from "Harmagedon: Genma Wars" was part of the genesis of Chun-Li.

Boxer, Ryu, Ken, Sagat, and Zangief were inspired by real life athletes, respectively Mike Tyson, Mas Oyama, Joe Lewis, Sagat Petchyindee, and Victor Zangiev Zhanghief.

> **Trivia:** Originally called M. Bison, the boxer was renamed to "Balrog" for the US release, out of lawsuit concerns from the American heavy-weight boxing champion.

For the backgrounds, Hollywood and VHS cassettes came to the rescue.

> I remember stitching together a few movies to make a presentation. "Streets of Fire" and Charles Bronson's "Hard Times" were the ones I used back then. Basically movies about fighting.
>
> I really took the chairman's words to heart – "Use movies!" he said, so I took that to mean we should just openly plagiarize them!
>
> — Akiman[21]

Employees did not get paid to watch one movie. They got paid to watch three!

> We didn't have a whole lot of time, so we had a 3-monitor set-up where we could watch other movies at the same time.
>
> We did as the president told us: - "Watch them all and learn from them!".
>
> — NiN[21]

> **Trivia:** Coincidentally, the Japanese title of "Hard Times" was "The Street Fighter".

4.5 Shapes and Sprites

This historical detour was important in order to understand the sheet system. With this knowledge we can review the last GFX ROM requirements involving OBJs.

On this layer, tiles can be used either directly or in groups which mandate distinct layout in GFXROM.

Ken stage inspiration

Ken stage sketch[57]

Ken stage as seen in the game

4.5.1 Sprite

A sprite is a collection of tiles with rectangular boundaries. As we will see in the m68k programming section it can be rendered by issuing a single draw call mentioning the offset in the sheet, the width in tiles and the height in tiles.

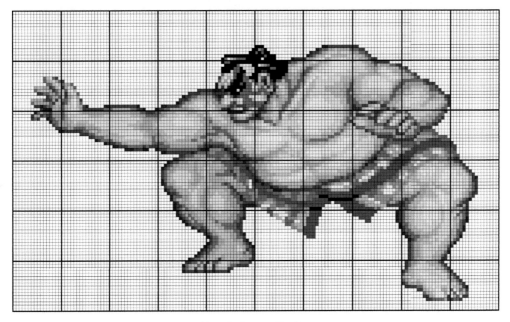

Honda has a Sprite

While it is convenient to be able to use a single command and the best way to render a set of mostly opaque tiles, it is inefficient. A set of tiles where many are transparent not only wastes precious storage space in the GFXROM, it also counts against the CPS-A/CPS-B limit of 256 tiles per frame.

Another limitation (or advantage depending on how you look at it) is that a single palette is specified when placing the sprite draw command so all tiles must use it.

4.5.2 Shape

A much more efficient and flexible method is to use a Shape where tile layout can be arbitrary. It takes several draw calls to draw (tiles have to be specified one by one) but they can be located anywhere in a GFXROM.

Shapes have the triple advantage of saving storage space, narrowing down tile count during rendition to the minimum, and allowing per tile palettes. The example of Honda shows that only 41 tiles are required as a Shape. It would have taken 60 tiles if a Sprite had been used.

> **Trivia:** In Street Fighter II, artists limited themselves to one palette per character because the OBJ layer was used for multiple things such as decoration and GUI. This was purely a design decision. They could have as well gone with 16 palettes per character since they are drawn with Shape instead of Sprite commands.

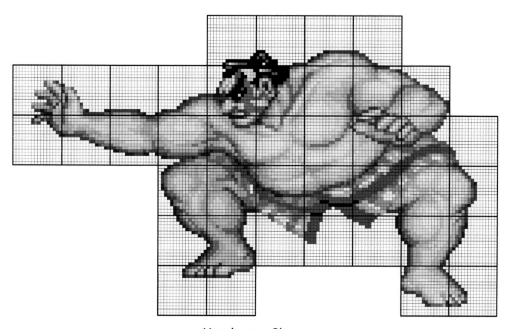

Honda as a Shape

To allow sprite draw calls, the build system must allocate images depending on the intended usage. All tiles in a sprite must be placed as they appeared in the original image.

The look of Capcom sheets is deceiving. Tiles in the OBJ layers are arranged in a visual coherent fashion which could lead one to assume they are rendered as Sprites. However this was only done to keep track of allocations, most Capcom games render OBJs as Shapes. Modern tools do not have this problem.

On page 164 is a Honda sheet featuring the same artwork twice. It is featured first as a Sprite, at `0x00` where it appears like a rectangle. It appears a second time as a Shape. Thanks to the automatic allocator in `ccps`, tiles are placed as they were encountered when reading the asset. It looks like mashed potatoes but uses less space.

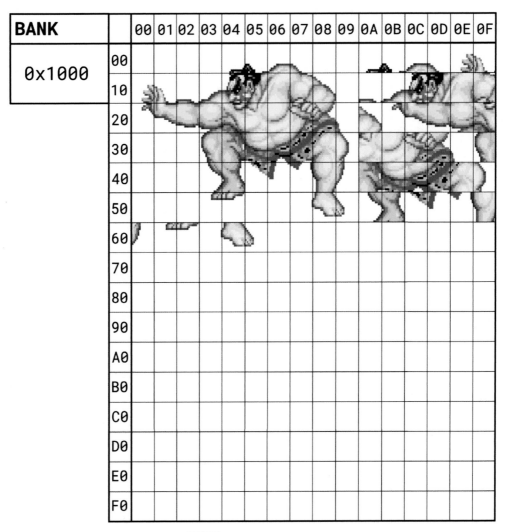

A sheet, generated with `ccps`, with a Sprite Honda and a Shape Honda

Sound System

Making ROMs for the sound system is a little bit more complicated than for the GFX system.

Not only are samples and music assets processed, there is also a need to compile code to bootstrap and then run the z80. This program is commonly called a "Sound Driver".

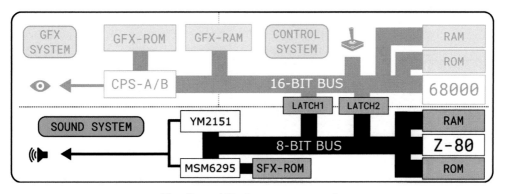

The Sound System components

The assets and the driver must be packed into two ROMs, one called "z80 ROM" and another called "OKI ROM". This asymmetry where three systems result in two ROMs is further complicated by the dependency graph that looks like a plate of spaghetti.

The difficult part is that both sound effects and music contribute to the OKI ROM content which must be populated in two steps.

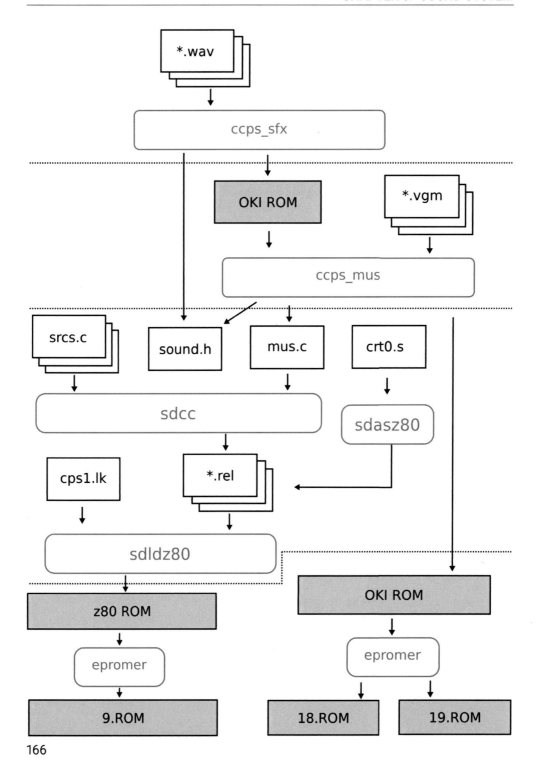

The structure of the OKI ROM facilitates the task since it features an index at the beginning which references all payloads. Leveraging it allows a first pass where audio samples are ingested by the build system to generate an incomplete OKI ROM. In a second pass, the music tracks are processed so new samples are added to the index ROM and the payload appended.

At the very top, `ccps_sfx` expects artists to provide sound samples contained in `.wav` files, a format which is universally supported by audio tools. This stage generates a partial OKI ROM and a `.h` header file to be injected in the control build graph so the m68k can request sample playback with a simple ID.

The second stage involves `ccps_mus`, the music processor. It expects `.vgm` (Video Game Music) from which are extracted raw YM2151 instructions. It outputs the final OKI ROM with the sample used by the soundtrack and also a `.c` file including bytecode containing YM2151 register values, timing, and OKI sample timing.

The last stage relies on the Small Device C Compiler (SDCC) toolchain. All artifacts generated in the previous stages are used along with the inputs for the sound driver (`.c` files) and the bootstrap `crt0.s` assembled by `sdasz80` assembler. In this step, all resulting relocatable object files `.rel` are linked together via ssdc's linker `sdldz80`.

5.1   Processing Sound Samples

A wav file is a simple container with a header describing the content followed by a payload. Once the sampling frequency, bits per sample, and number of channels is retrieved, the PCM can be accessed.

5.1.1   Constraint

Artists should not produce stereo wavs since the CPS-1 is mono. Moreover, game developers should decide if they wish to use the OKI in high quality (7575Hz) or low quality (6060Hz) and all assets should use that sampling rate. Finally, since ADPCM compressed 12-bit sample to 4-bit samples, artists should provide 16-bit wavs.

5.1.2   ADPCM Compression

Decompression is done in hardware by the OKI at runtime but the build system still has to compress assets appropriately.

ADPCM encodes the difference between the previous sample and the sample to be generated. Each 16-bit sample is downsampled to 12-bit and compressed to a 4-bit nibble[50].

```
int transitionTable[8] = {-1, -1, -1, -1, 2, 4, 6, 8};

int stepSizes[49] = {
    16,    17,    19,    21,    23,    25,    28,    31,    34,    37,
    41,    45,    50,    55,    60,    66,    73,    80,    88,    97,
   107,   118,   130,   143,   157,   173,   190,   209,   230,   253,
   279,   307,   337,   371,   408,   449,   494,   544,   598,   658,
   724,   796,   876,   963,  1060,  1166,  1282,  1411,  1552};

int stepSizeIndex = 0; // Initial value (0) points to 16
int16_t lastSample = 0;

int8_t compress(int16_t sample) {
    int8_t B3 = 0, B2 = 0, B1 = 0, B0 = 0; // Bit of the output nibble

    sample >>= 4; // Convert from 16-bit to 12-bit
    int16_t diff = sample - lastSample;

    if (diff < 0) B3 = 1; // Set magnitude sign bit
    diff = abs(diff);

    int16_t ss = stepSizes[stepSizeIndex];

    if (diff >= ss)   B2 = 1, diff -=  ss;    // Set B2
    if (diff >= ss/2) B1 = 1, diff -= (ss/2); // Set B1
    if (diff >= ss/4) B0 = 1;                 // Set B0

    int8_t nibble = B3 << 3 | B2 << 2 | B1 << 1 | B0;

    // Keep track of the value upon decompression
    lastSample = decompress(lastSample, nibble, stepSizeIndex);

    stepSizeIndex += transitionTable[nibble & 0x7];
    return nibble;
}
```

Let's take an example converting a stream of 16-bit PCM to 4-bit ADPCM nibbles.

```
short pcm[4] = {960, 960, 950, 160};
```

168

Compressing sample 1

The first 16-bit sample has a value of `960` which becomes `60` in 12-bit. With the current step size at 16, ADPCM can only command a delta of + (16 + 16/2 + 16/4) = +28 which it encodes in a nibble `0b0111`. The step size index is updated via the transitionTable[`b111`] = 8. The current step size is `34`.

Compressing sample 2

The second 16-bit sample also has a value of `960` which becomes `60` in 12-bit. Since the latest sample output was 28, ADPCM must somehow encode a difference of 60-28 = 32. ADPCM commands a delta of + (0 + 34/2 + 34/4) = +25 which it encodes in a nibble `0b0011`.

The decompressor will output 28 (its last value) + 25 = 53. We can see how the step size has adapted to the delta requested with only two steps.

The step size index is updated via 8 (previous value) -1 (transitionTable[`b011`]) = 7. Now the step size is `31`.

Compressing sample 3

The third 16-bit sample has a value of `950` which becomes `59` in 12-bit. Since the latest sample output was 53, ADPCM encodes a difference of 59-53 = 6. ADPCM commands a delta of + (0 + 0 + 0) = 0 which it encodes in a nibble `0b0000`.

The decompressor will output 53 (its last value) + 0 = 53. The step size index is updated via 7 (previous value) - 1 (transitionTable[`b000`]) = 6. Now the step size is `28`.

Compressing sample 4

The last 16-bit sample has a value of `160` which becomes `10` in 12-bit. Since the latest sample output was 53, ADPCM encodes a difference of 10-53 = -43. ADPCM commands a delta of - (28 + 28/2 + 0) = -42 which it encodes in a nibble `0b1110`.

The decompressor will output 53 (its last value) - 42 = 11. The step size index is updated via 6 (previous value) + 6 (transitionTable[`0b110`]) = 12. Now the step size is `50`.

Graphing PCM vs ADPCM shows that the decompressed stream "lags" behind upon abrupt changes but catches up aggressively. ADPCM first value is always near zero (+/-28) but it is not audible to players since most samples start with a fade-in.

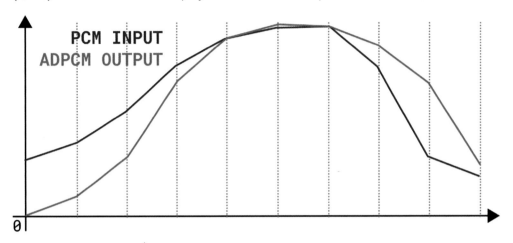

5.2   Structure of the OKI ROM

The structure of the OKI is simple. It features a 127 * 6 bytes table at its beginning. Each entry points to a payload in the ROM. The payload of each entry must be a ADPCM stream.

For some reason offset 0 in the table index must not be used.

```
typedef struct {
  uint8_t firstOffset[3];
  uint8_t unused;
  uint8_t lastOffset[3];
  uint8_t unused;
} oki_entry;

typedef struct {
  uint8_t unused[8]
  oki_entry entries[127]
  uint8_t payload[0x3FC00]
}
```

Notice there is no metadata to indicate the bitrate. The "database" entry is a plain offset directly pointing to ADPCM nibbles. It is up to the build system to carry out this info to the z80. In practice, Capcom games never mixed bitrate and always used 7575Hz.

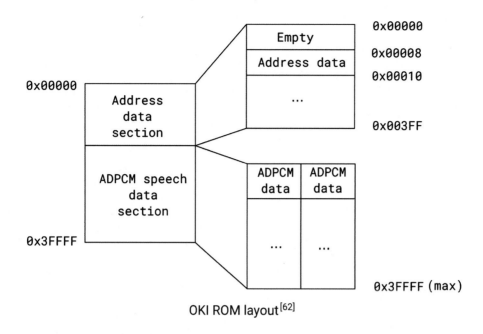

OKI ROM layout[62]

5.3 Processing Music

Making music with FM synthesis is an art which this book does not intend to butcher. The best way to go is to ask the musicians in the team to work with whatever tool they wish (the amazing DefleMask is highly recommended) and export their symphonies using VGM file format.

VGM (Video Game Music) is a community effort originating from `smspower.org` to create an audio file format able to support many legacy systems (SEGA consoles, MSX, Neo Geo, and PC) as well as arcade hardware.

The arcade profile is particularly interesting for CPS-1 development since it uses YM2151 for FM Synthesis and SegaPCM for the samples.

While the YM2151 is obviously a perfect fit that will need no processing, the SegaPCM needs some adjustments. As a chip used by SEGA in their AM2 (Amusement Machine 2) from 1985 to 1991, it is superior in capabilities to the MSM6295. It relies on 16-bit PCM, up to 32kHz sampling, has more channels, and has a larger address space.

The build system can take care of compressing the SegaPCM to ADPCM and resampling from 32KHz to 8080Hz but the musicians should only use two channels for music samples in order to play nicely with the CPS-1, where the two other channels are used to play sound effects.

```
// List of VGM bytecode converted to miniVGM bytecode.
0x54 | aa dd | Write dd to YM2151 register aa.       -> MUSIC_NOTE
0x61 | nn nn | Wait n samples (0 to 1.49 seconds). -> DELAY
0x62 |       | Wait 735 samples (60th of a second) -> DELAY
0x63 |       | Wait 882 samples (50th of a second).-> DELAY
0x66 |       | End of sound data.                    -> END_SONG
0xC0 |bbaa dd| Write dd to Sega PCM register aabb. -> MUSIC_SOUND
```

5.4 Programming the z80

Programming Zilog's CPU into a sound driver involves doing two things right: bootstrapping and setup of the memory map. Since the latter is easier, it is discussed first. To avoid page turning, the requirements are reproduced here.

Start	End	Size	Function
0x0000	0x7FFF	32 KiB	ROM (32 KiB out of 64 KiB)
0x8000	0xBFFF	16 KiB	Bank-switched view of rest of ROM
0xD000	0xD7FF	2 KiB	RAM
0xF000	0xF001	2 B	YM2151 registers
0xF002	0xF002	1 B	OKI OKI6295 registers
0xF004	0xF004	1 B	Bank Switch control (SOU1)
0xF006	0xF006	1 B	OKI MSM6295 H / L mode
0xF008	0xF008	1 B	Sound commands (latch 1)
0xF00A	0xF00A	1 B	Sound commands (latch 2)

z80 memory map

Using `sdcc` helps a lot here since it features an exclusive "placement" keyword `__at`.

```
__at(0xF000) char REG_YM2151_ADR;
__at(0xF001) char REG_YM2151_DAT;
__at(0xF002) char REG_OKI;
__at(0xF004) char REG_BANK_SWITCH;
__at(0xF006) char REG_OKY_QUALITY_SWITCH;
__at(0xF008) char REG_LATCH1;
__at(0xF00A) char REG_LATCH2;
```

With the registers correctly mapped, what remains is to place `.text` and `.data` at the right locations in ROM. This can easily be done thanks to the awesome `sdldz80` linker and its linker script.

```
-mjwx
-i out/main.ihx
-b _CODE = 0x0200
-b _DATA = 0xd000
-k /usr/share/sdcc/lib/z80
-l z80
out/crt0.rel
out/main.rel

-e
```

As expected, the `_DATA` is placed at `0xd000`. The `_CODE` however is placed not at `0x0000` but `0x0200` for reasons that will follow soon.

> **Trivia:** Debugging a CPS-1 program can be a tedious task. A good starting point when encountering an issue is to read the linker `.map` file which indicates where each symbol was placed.

5.4.1 Bootstrapping

A z80 starts fetching and executing instructions from address `0x0000`. The bootstrap code `crt0.s` (on page 174) is placed accordingly via directive `.org 0`. The code immediately jumps to `0x100` in order to skip the interrupt handler instructions.

The z80 can work in interrupt modes 0, 1, or 2. Modes 0 and 2 are the most powerful and complex but they imply retrieving the ID of the interrupting peripheral by reading a byte on the data bus. This mechanism allows support of multi-device interruption. However in this case, it is overkill. The z80 uses Mode 1 which always makes the CPU jump to `0x38` when interrupted.

At `.org 0x100`, the stack pointer `sp` is set to point at the end of `RAM` (the z80 stack grows downward), the first interrupt is requested and a mystery `gsinit` function is called. All the code in `crt0.s` accounts for a few hundred bytes. Which explains why we requested the linker script to place `_CODE` further at `0x200`.

> **Trivia:** The calling functions from ASM to C require using `_` prefixed symbols.

```
.module crt0
.globl  _main
.globl  _interrupt
.globl  _schedInterrupt
.area   _HEADER (ABS)


;------------------
; Z-80 starts here!
;------------------
.org 0
    jp init



;------------------
;  INTERRUPT HANDLER
;------------------
.org 0x38
    DI                            ; Disable Interrupt
    call _interrupt               ; Process Interrupt
    call _schedInterrupt          ; Reschedule interrupt
    EI                            ; Enable  Interrupt
    RET


;--------------
;  INIT and MAIN
;--------------
.org 0x100
init:

    ld   sp,#0xd7ff               ; Setup stack
    IM 1                          ; Set Interupt mode 1
    call _schedInterrupt          ; Request first int
    call  gsinit                  ; Init global variables
main:
    call  _main                   ; Call C main()
    jp    main                    ; Never happens
```

5.4.2 z80 interrupt

In order to interact with the latches properly but also be able to keep track of wall-time, the z80 needs to be interrupted regularly. Zilog's CPU does features a timer RFSH but it is intended for DRAM refresh (which the sound system does not feature anyway).

Instead the interrupts are triggered by the YM2151, thanks to its two internal timers.

Timer A is a 10-bit counter while Timer B is an 8-bit counter. For a YM2151 running at 3,579Hz, the trigger formula is 64 * (1024 - value) / 3579.

Setting the Timer A to `800` will result in an interrupt 64 * (1024 - 800) / 3579 = 4ms later. When the YM2151 counter reaches zero, it asserts a line connected to the z80 `INT` line which makes the CPU jump to address `0x38`.

```
void waitYM2151() {
  while (REG_YM2151_DAT == 0x80) {
    // Wait until YM2151 is ready for write
  }
}

void interrupt() {
  // Read latches here
}

void schedInterrupt() { // Schedule an interrupt in 4ms
  waitYM2151 ();
  REG_YM2151_ADR = 0x10; // Register Timer A 8 MSB
  REG_YM2151_DAT = 0xC8; // 0b11001000

  waitYM2151 ();
  REG_YM2151_ADR = 0x11; // Register Timer A 2 LSB
  REG_YM2151_DAT = 0x00; // 0b00
}
```

5.4.3 Initializing variables

To finish bootstrapping, `crt0` makes sure initialized C variable values are set. The linker placed all values requiring initialization in a `_GSINIT` segment. By wrapping it with markers `_INITIALIZER` (src) and `_INITIALIZED` (dst), they can be copied easily.

```
; Ordering of segments for the linker.
.area _HOME
.area _CODE
.area _INITIALIZER
.area _GSINIT
.area _GSFINAL
.area _DATA
.area _INITIALIZED
.area _HEAP
```

Copying is done with `ldir` instruction using the linker macros. Prefix `s_` refers to the "start" of a segment while prefix `l_` refers to the "length" of that segment.

```
.area _GSINIT                ; Initialize global variables
gsinit:                      ; Copy values from ROM > RAM.
    ld   bc, #l__INITIALIZER
    ld   a, b
    or   a, c
    jr   Z, gsinit_next
    ld   de, #s__INITIALIZED
    ld   hl, #s__INITIALIZER
    ldir
gsinit_next:
    ret
```

5.4.4   z80 Sound Driver

The sound driver is a simple loop which reads bytecode from our mini-vgm format to feed music notes, no-op on pauses, and forwards sample playback.

```
int8_t noopCounter = 0;

void updateMusic() {
  if (noopCounter) { // Does the YM2151 need a break?
    noopCounter--;     // 14ms increment.
    return;
  }
next_byte_code:
  int8_t bc = next();
  switch (bc) { // Use our custom bytecode (miniVGM).
    case DELAY :
       noopCounter = bc; break;
    case MUSIC_NOTE :
       REG_YM2151_ADR = next();
       REG_YM2151_DAT = next();
       goto next_byte_code;
    case MUSIC_SOUND :
       REG_OKI = 0x8 | next();
       REG_OKI = next();
       goto next_byte_code;
    case END_SONG: // End of song
       stopMusic(); break;
  }
}
```

A single latch is used to received commands as "immediate value". If bit 0x80 is set, control is requesting a sound effect to be played, otherwise it is music.

The `main` uses an "active" loop in order to never outpace the `interrupt` function call frequency. This guarantees it runs in the vicinity of 250Hz.

```
int8_t intCounter = 0;
int8_t latch;


void interrupt () {
    intCounter++;
    latch = REG_LATCH1;
}

// Incremtend by the main() function.
int8_t  musCounter = 0;

// Incremented by the interrupt() function.
volatile int8_t  lastLatch;


void main () {
  while(true) {
    musCounter++;

    // Only tick after interrupt ticks
    while (musCounter < intCounter) {
    }

    updateMusic(); // Feed the YM2151 or skip for pause.

    if (latch == 0xFF) continue;
    if (latch == lastLatch) continue;
    lastLatch = latch;

    // Forward to OKI
    if (latch & 0x80) {
      REG_OKI = 0x8  | latch;
      // 0x10 = Channel 1, 0x00 = Max volume.
      REG_OKI = 0x10 | 0x00; // TODO: Round-robin on channels.
    } else {
      setupMusicPlayback(latch & 0x70);
    }
  }
}
```

5.5 Back in the Days

From its inception, Capcom recognized the crucial importance of sound for a video-game and set out to hire the very best musicians they could find.

By 1989, they had assembled a pool of talent who called themselves the "Capcom Sound Team".

The Capcom Sound team. L-R: Yoko Shimomura, Yoshihiro Sakaguchi, Manami Matsumae, Masaki Izumiya, Yasuaki Fujita, Mari Yamaguchi, Minae Fujii, Toshio Kajino, and Isao Abe. Identity of table-man is unknown.

5.5.1 Recruiting

Capcom actively recruited by taking advantage of 'careers days' to get graduates to come work for them. Many musicians emerged from music schools located in the Kansai region encompassing Kyoto, Osaka, and Kobe near Capcom headquarters.

Several alumni of Osaka College of Music ended up working for Capcom, where they were able to compose music for a living while having the security of working for a large Japanese company.

One of these recruits, Yoko Shimomura, would go on to compose music for games such as Street Fighter II, Final Fight, and Final Fantasy. She gave numerous interviews which help to paint a picture of the life of a musician working at Capcom.

> I studied piano in college, but I loved the Famicom, and would often stay up all night playing it.
>
> Then the next day my shoulders would be all stiff, and my piano teacher would scold me, and my Mom even said "I don't remember raising a daughter like this."
>
> I decided that when I graduated, I would go work at a place where I could play both music and Famicom all day without complaints!
>
> — Yoko Shimomura, Capcom Sound team [47]

Yoko's account of her hiring interview confirms that Capcom was more interested in hiring talented musicians than tech savvy people.

> I did not know you could write music with a computer until I joined the company. At the entrance exam, I was asked "what sequencer do you use?" and I had to ask back "What? Is that like an electronic controller?".
>
> They had to teach me from the ground up, and after that it was less musical practice than it was technical. The first music data I turned in was thoroughly corrected, and I was feeling really glum.
>
> I was asked to talk about what I knew about FM generation at the entrance exam. I had no idea what it was, so I thought about AM/FM radio and wrote down "it sounds better these days than it used to."
>
> — Yoko Shimomura, Capcom Sound team [47]

5.5.2 Creative Process

Even though musicians were part of a "Sound Team", they usually worked alone on a game.

They could pick projects based on availability [58] but they were assigned to the next one immediately after they were done with the previous one.

Being dropped in a project and asked to write music was difficult. It was mostly the planner's responsibility to brief the musician on what kind of music they wanted[65].

> NiN would come up to me and show me designs of the characters and explain the personalities of the characters and ask me to make theme songs for each character.
>
> I would look at the backgrounds and the character descriptions and all that, and I noticed that each character had a unique background. And because of that, I suggested making each theme song based on their background country and culture.
>
> — Yoko Shimomura, Capcom Sound team[45]

The work ethic of the composers had nothing to envy to the artists drawing pixels.

> At 11 o'clock, all the security was activated and you could not move between floors. The elevators stopped moving too. If you had to finish work by 7 o'clock the next day, we had to pass ROM down from the window on a string.
>
> Once I tied a carrier bag and put the ROM inside and gave it to them. 15 mn later, the phone rang. They said "sorry but we broke the pins when we put it in! Can you give us another?"
>
> — Yoko Shimomura, Capcom Sound team[66]

5.5.3 Tools

Yoshihiro Sakaguchi, author of Mega Man music, explained what computer the musicians connected to their Yamaha keyboards.

> We worked on both the music and sound effects for Capcom's games. We've got a centralized recording system setup on a PC-98, so that even if we're writing music for different hardware, we can compose without needing to be able to program.
>
> — Yoshihiro Sakaguchi[46]

NEC PC-9800 series

NEC entered the personal computer market in 1979 with its 8800 series. These machines, built around 8-bit z80 CPUs would later be known as "PC-88".

Thanks to its optional kanji ROM, NEC quickly gained traction. The PC-88 accounted for 40% of the Japanese personal market by 1981.

By the mid-80s, the aging series was discontinued in favor of machines based on 16-bit Intel CPUs such as the i286. The NEC's next computer, named 9801, was be the first in the 9800 line. These machines were commonly referred to as "PC-98".

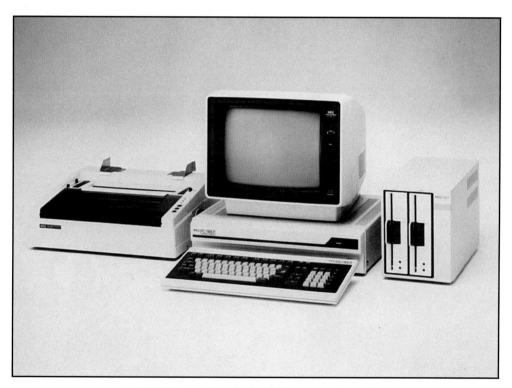

PC-9801, the first in the 9800 series (1984)

Like the PC-88, the PC-98 enjoyed considerable success. Over its lifespan ranging from 1992 to 2000, NEC sold more than 18 million units. Across multiple lines such as "Desktop", "Hi-end", or "Laptop", NEC released a new machine every year[68].

The success was such that the series accounted for 60% of the Japanese Personal Computer market by 1991.

What Capcom used

Because so many models were released, it is hard to tell for sure which PC-98 was used for a particular game. What can be done is to list the models released each year in order to get a rough idea.

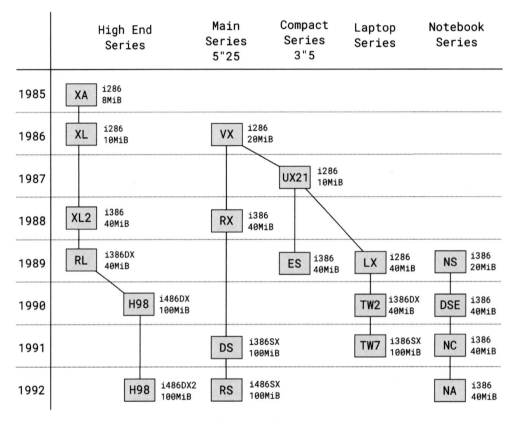

	High End Series	Main Series 5"25	Compact Series 3"5	Laptop Series	Notebook Series
1985	XA i286 8MiB				
1986	XL i286 10MiB	VX i286 20MiB			
1987			UX21 i286 10MiB		
1988	XL2 i386 40MiB	RX i386 40MiB			
1989	RL i386DX 40MiB		ES i386 40MiB	LX i286 40MiB	NS i386 20MiB
1990	H98 i486DX 100MiB			TW2 i386DX 40MiB	DSE i386 40MiB
1991		DS i386SX 100MiB		TW7 i386SX 100MiB	NC i386 40MiB
1992	H98 i486DX2 100MiB	RS i486SX 100MiB			NA i386 40MiB

A selection of PC-98s from 1985 to 1992

It is likely musicians working on CPS-1 titles were provided with computers from the Main series. Around that time, it would have been a computer based on a Intel 386 CPU with 50 MiB HDD.

Proprietary technology

Despite their name, NEC's machine had nothing to do with the IBM PC. Due to its operating system, MS-DOS, lacking support for Japanese glyphs, Big Blue's machines never managed to break into the Japanese market. NEC's PCs were named after what they were, **P**ersonal **C**omputers.

C-Bus

The PC-98 uses a proprietary 16-bit C-bus instead of the IBM's ISA bus. BIOS, I/O port addressing, memory management and graphics output are also different. This architecture was both a moat that protected NEC from clone manufacturers (which plagued IBM in the USA) and a dungeon that prevented its machine from benefiting from the many peripherals built for IBM PCs.

It was an extra effort for manufactures to create C-bus version of their card but companies such as Roland and Creative did release some of their sound cards for PC-98.

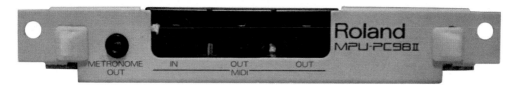

A C-bus Roland MIDI card for PC98II

Video chip

Besides their proprietary bus, PC-98s were noteworthy for their, at the time, powerful graphic system.

The heart of it was the High-Performance Graphics Display Controller 7220, more commonly known as μPD7220. The PC-98 used two of them, both running 2.5MHz. One handled the 8 KiB VRAM for text while the other acted as a co-processor managing a 96 KiB VRAM framebuffer.

The tandem was one of the first GPUs, presenting primitives to draw lines, circles, arcs, and character graphics. In its highest resolution mode the PC-98 reached an impressive 640×400 with 8 colors. It allowed Latin alphabetic, numeric and most importantly katakana characters. An optional ROM board added 3,000 kanji glyphs to the repertory.

The end of PC-98

Although having specs far inferior to the Fujitsu FM Towns and Sharp X68000, NEC enjoyed tremendous success, selling 18 million units from 1982 to 1999.

A list accounting for games-only still totals 1,228 titles. Proof of the machine's status as a game developer's favorite.

NEC's domination only started to wane when DOS/V, a special version of Microsoft's MS-DOS supporting Japanese characters, came out at the end of 1990.

Control System

The control system is the simplest ROM to build since it involves only compiling code and the hardest to get right because of the complexity of its dependencies and the components it needs to communicate with.

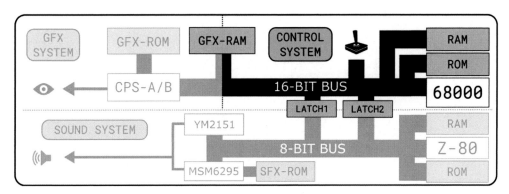

The control system components

While the latch toward the Sound system is a small API surface, the GFX API is huge. The interface to the Graphic System is bigger both in breadth (it features 64 registers) and depth (the expected GFXRAM data layout is non-trivial).

To our advantage, the Motorola 68000 is a target supported by the **G**NU **C**ompiler **C**ollection (GCC). This suite features a much more powerful linker script system than `sdcc` which helps considerably to solve the memory mapping requirements.

All stages of the build graph rely on tools provided by GNU GCC. Compiling `.c` code to `.obj` is done via `gcc` compiler. Assembling `.s` files to `.obj` files is taken care of by `as` assembler . Finally, the `ld` linker combines all `.obj` together into raw instructions.

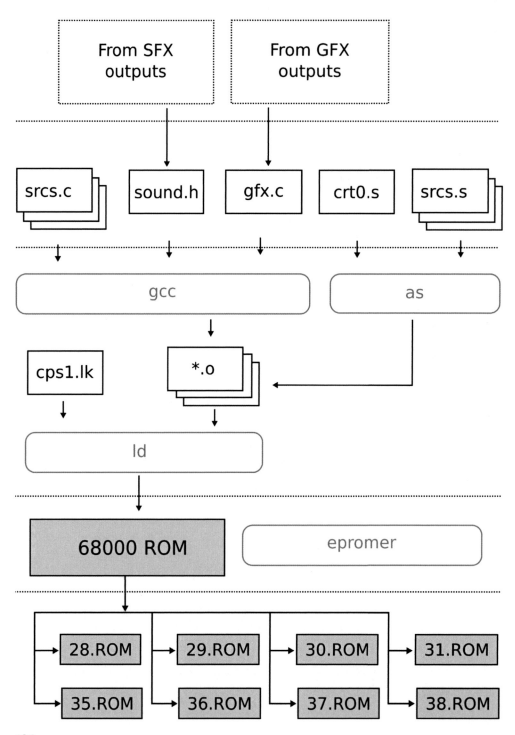

At the end of the process, the logical m68k ROM is split into interleaved chip-sized ROMs according to the specifics of the target board (described in the hardware chapter).

Like the z80, bootstrapping is solved with a small assembler program named `crt0.s`.

6.1 Bootstrapping the 68000

Contrary to a z80, a m68k does not have a set booting address. Instead, it reads an array of 64 32-bit integers called the "vector table". Located at `0x000000`, this is where the CPU finds the values to initialize its registers such as the stack pointer (offset `0`) and instruction pointer (offset `1`).

```
.extern main

dc.l 0xFFF000, _boot,    Def, Def, Def, Def, Def, Def
dc.l        Def,    Def,    Def, Def, Def, Def, Def, Def
dc.l        Def,    Def,    Def, Def, Def, Def, Def, Def
dc.l        Def,    Def, VSync, Def, Def, Def, Def, Def
dc.l        Def,    Def,    Def, Def, Def, Def, Def, Def
dc.l        Def,    Def,    Def, Def, Def, Def, Def, Def
dc.l        Def,    Def,    Def, Def, Def, Def, Def, Def
dc.l        Def,    Def,    Def, Def, Def, Def, Def, Def

.align 4
Def:
 rte
```

All other slots except for one (offset `26`) point to a no-op routine.

6.2 Auto-Interrupt

The 68000 has multiple interrupt modes. In its most complex form, `IPL0`, `IPL1`, and `IPL2` encode a level of interrupt and the interrupt ID is retrieved via an external interrupt controller. This would be over-kill for the task at hand.

A simpler mode, auto-vector, makes the CPU jump directly based on the three IPL lines' state. Three lines are treated as bits giving a value within [0,7], which is used to look up the "vector table" starting at offset `24`.

The 3-bit scheme uses `IPL0` for bit 0, `IPL1` for bit 1, and `IPL2` for bit 2. With CPS-A INT only connected to `IPL1`, handler #2 is always called upon interrupt. Therefore, VSync must be placed at offset `24 + 2 = 26`.

```
# VSYNC interrupt handler, jumps to C function.
.align 4
VSync:
    jsr onVSync
  rte
```

The last piece of the `_boot` function sets up auto-vector mode and jump to `main`.

```
.align 4
_boot:
    * Enable auto-interrupts
    move.w   #0x2000, sr

    * Init .BSS
    jbsr     clearBSS

    * Init .DATA
    jbsr     copyDATA

    * Jump to C main()
    jbsr     main
```

6.3 Memory Map

Like for the Sound System and its z80 memory space, we need to make sure the software behaves according to the memory map defined by the board PALs.

The compiler in the GNU Compiler Collection, `gcc` does not have a placement keyword `__at` but even if it had been available, it would not have been enough to map large portions such as the 192 KiB of GFXRAM.

We can compensate for the lack of `__at` thanks to the power of `ld`'s linker script system. The idea is to use a two step method:

1. Define memory regions in the script thanks to the `MEMORY` keyword. Create segments where code/data are stored in regions based on read/write access types.

2. Connect regions and segments in the C code.

6.3.1 Goal

To avoid flipping pages, here is the memory map studied on page 53.

Start	End	Size	Function
0x000000	0x3FFFFF	4 MiB	ROM
0x800000	0x800007	8 B	JAMMA Players Inputs
0x800018	0x80001F	8 B	JAMMA Dip Switches
0x800030	0x800037	8 B	JAMMA Coin sensors
0x800176	0x800177	1 B	Kick harness
0x800100	0x80013f	64 B	CPS-A registers
0x800140	0x80017f	64 B	CPS-B registers
0x800180	0x800187	8 B	Sound commands (latch 1)
0x800188	0x80018F	8 B	Sound commands (latch 2)
0x900000	0x92FFFF	192 KiB	GFXRAM
0xFF0000	0xFFFFFF	64 KiB	RAM

6.3.2 Memory Regions

```
OUTPUT_FORMAT("binary")
OUTPUT_ARCH(m68k)
MEMORY {
  /* Define memory regions */
  rom (rx)     : ORIGIN = 0x000000, LENGTH = 0x200000
  jamma_p(rw) : ORIGIN = 0x800000, LENGTH = 0x8
  jamma_d(rw) : ORIGIN = 0x800018, LENGTH = 0x8
  jamma_c(rw) : ORIGIN = 0x800030, LENGTH = 0x8
  kick_a(rw)  : ORIGIN = 0x800176, LENGTH = 0x8
  cpsa_reg(rw): ORIGIN = 0x800100, LENGTH = 0x40
  cpsb_reg(rw): ORIGIN = 0x800140, LENGTH = 0x40
  latch_1(rw) : ORIGIN = 0x800180, LENGTH = 0x8
  latch_2(rw) : ORIGIN = 0x800188, LENGTH = 0x8
  gfx_ram(rw) : ORIGIN = 0x900000, LENGTH = 0x2FFFF
  ram (rw)    : ORIGIN = 0xFF0000, LENGTH = 0xFFFF
}
```

Trivia: Notice how powerful the linker script is compared to `sdcc`. A directive `OUTPUT_FORMAT (" binary ")` allows outputting raw binary without using a container like `elf`. This avoids the conversion step from elf to binary using `objcopy`.

```
SECTIONS {

  .text : {
    *(.text)
    _etext = . ;
    . = ALIGN(4);
  } > rom

  .data : {
    _data = . ;        // Start of .data marker
    *(.data)
    _edata = . ;       // End  of .data marker
    . = ALIGN(4);
  } > rom AT> ram      // LMA = rom but VMA = ram

  .rodata : {
    *(.rodata)
    *(.rodata.*)
    . = ALIGN(4);
  } > rom

  .gfx_data : {
  } > gfx_ram

  .cpsa_reg : {
  } > cpsa_reg

  .cpsb_reg : {
  } > cpsb_reg

  .bss : {
    _bss = .;          // Start of .bss marker
    *(.bss)
    _ebss = .;         // End  of .bss marker
    . = ALIGN(4);
  } > ram
  ...
}
```

In the second part of the script, sections are assigned (via >) to a memory region using their MEMORY name.

Trivia: Notice the care taken to make sure the 68000 will only attempt to access aligned data via `.ALIGN(4)` directives. Unaligned memory access is an unrecoverable error resulting in the 68000 `HALT`ing.

6.3.3   Code to segment

C variables are placed into these sections using the names defined in the linker script.

```
#define ALIGN(X) __attribute__ ((aligned (X)))
#define GFXRAM __attribute__ ((section (".gfx_data")))
#define CPSA   __attribute__ ((section (".cpsa_reg")))
#define CPSB   __attribute__ ((section (".cpsb_reg")))
// ... All other SECTIONS here.

GFXRAM ALIGN(256) short palettes[6 * 32 * 16];
CPSA   short cpsa_reg[0x20] = {};
CPSB   short cpsb_reg[0x20] = {};
// ... All memory mapped data structures here.
```

6.4   Initializing variables

The linker script created markers and requested section `.data` to be written to `rom`
(VMA) but relocated symbols (via **AT>**) as if they were in `ram` (LMA).

With these elements, zeroing the bss and populating `.data` with initial values is just a
few lines of C.

```
// These are defined by the linker via the linker script
extern char _etext _data, _edata, _bss, _ebss;

char *src = &_etext;
char *dst = &_data;

// Copy ROM to DATA
void copyDATA() {
  while (dst < &_edata) {
    *dst++ = *src++;
  }
}

// Zero BSS.
void clearBSS() {
  for (dst = &_bss; dst< &_ebss; dst++) {
    *dst = 0;
  }
}
```

6.5   Verifying RAM

Our bootloader is simple but the ones used by Capcom did more than bringing up the CPUs. They also verify the health of hardware components. These screens are rarely, if ever, seen by players since they are visible only once when the cabinet is turned on. During normal operations, that would be when nobody is there.

All CPS-1 games display a slightly different set of text. However all of them check for faulty RAM access by the Control system. By checking the communication lines, the cabinet prevented wild goose bug hunts where a sub-system would fault because it received corrupted messages.

By quickly ruling out a whole class of errors, the startup tests sped up debugging and brought down repairing costs.

The technique used is simple. For all bytes in each area of the RAM and GFXRAM, the m68k tries to write a value, then tries to read it back. If they differ, the memory is faulty and an error message is displayed.

The limit of this technique is that only what is visible to the Control system can be verified. There is no way to checksum the GFXROM. While the z80 can access most of the Sound System ROM (except for the OKI ROM), it could perform checks but would have no way to surface errors since the latches can only be written from the m68k side.

Ghouls 'n Ghosts boot screen

Street Fighter 2 boot screen

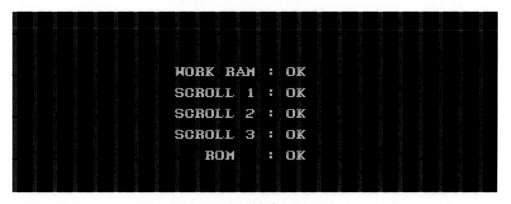

Forgotten Worlds boot screen

COLOR RAM   OK

WORK RAM   OK

SCROLL 1   OK

SCROLL 2   OK

SCROLL 3   OK

OBJ RAM   OK

Final Fight boot screen

6.6 Ruling them all

With each chapter peeling away a layer of complexity, we have finally reached the heart of the CP-System. The function `main` is where developers will have their game engine convert player inputs into visual and audio outputs.

The architecture is much like the z80 sound system where two "threads" run in lock-step. Function `VSync` is awakened every 16ms via an interrupt. Its job is to read inputs and save them locally, read sound/music requests, and write them to the latch. Most importantly, it flips the GFXRAM double buffered SCROLL and OBJ descriptors.

> **Trivia:** The `frameCounter` variable paces the main thread so a new frame is only hosted every 16ms instead of rendering as fast as possible. It is also useful to keep track of wall-time to render animation and game logic properly.

6.6.1 Commanding sound

Requesting a sound or music playback is only about writing to a latch and forgetting about it. However special care is necessary if the engine requests multiple sounds during the same frame. If this were to happen the value in the latch could be overwritten before the z80 picked it up. The solution is to implement a queue system where commands are stored and fed one by one every frame.

Functions `VSync` and `main` run in lock-step via two counters. Main only runs after a sync has occurred. `Sync` is always one step ahead of main function.

```
volatile int vsyncCounter = 0;
volatile int frameCounter = 0;

// Called every 16ms
void VSync() {

  if (frameCounter != lastFrameCounter) {
    flipGFXRAMPointers(); // Flip GFX SCROLLs and OBJs.
    writeSoundLatch();    // dequeue and write latch
    readInputs();
    lastFrameCounter = frameCounter;
  }

  vsyncCounter++; // Unlock the main loop.
}
```

6.6.2 Main

```
volatile int lastFrameCounter = 0;

void hostFrame() {
    ... // Game engine render one visual and audio frame.
}

void main() {
  while(true) {
    if (frameCounter < vsyncCounter) continue;
    hostFrame(); // Run 16ms of gameplay
    frameCounter++;
  }
}
```

How `hostframe` is implemented is completely at the programmer's discretion. Capcom games used a common kernel framework made of tasks. Since there is no source of interrupt beside `vsync` they implemented a collaborative multi-tasking system where the stack and registers are stored/loaded as each task is executed.

To learn about the kernel and how it is used to run multi-task A.I bytecode and moving fireballs, check out the Street Fighter II Platinum source code[67].

6.6.3 Retrieving inputs

Besides joystick and buttons, the engine must recover inputs such as the dip settings, P1Start, P2Start, and most importantly detect coins being inserted.

> **Trivia:** Arcade operators could configure the difficulty of a game via DIP switches. In Street Fighter 2, eight configurations go from the easiest where 1 coin grants six credits to the hardest where four coins grant a single credit. There is even a "Free Play" mode which no amount of begging could convince them to enable[51].

The three DIP switches are called A, B, and C. As visible on page 40 each DIP has 8 switches responsible for flipping a bit in a byte. Recovering the configuration is as simple as reading a byte from the memory map.

> **Trivia:** In Street Fighter 2, DIP B is used to configure the difficulty level of the game ranging from 0 to 8 (4=default). Based on this value the AI selects appropriate sets of bytecode[52] script. Even in easy mode, the AI cheats by skipping "charging"[52].

Label	Memory Area	Address	Mask
P1_KEY_3	JAMMA Players Inputs	0x800000	0b01000000
P1_KEY_2	JAMMA Players Inputs	0x800000	0b00100000
P1_KEY_1	JAMMA Players Inputs	0x800000	0b00010000
P_UP	JAMMA Players Inputs	0x800000	0b00001000
P1_DOWN	JAMMA Players Inputs	0x800000	0b00000100
P1_LEFT	JAMMA Players Inputs	0x800000	0b00000010
P1_RIGHT	JAMMA Players Inputs	0x800000	0b00000001
P2_KEY_3	JAMMA Players Inputs	0x800001	0b01000000
P2_KEY_2	JAMMA Players Inputs	0x800001	0b00100000
P2_KEY_1	JAMMA Players Inputs	0x800001	0b00010000
P2_UP	JAMMA Players Inputs	0x800001	0b00001000
P2_DOWN	JAMMA Players Inputs	0x800001	0b00000100
P2_LEFT	JAMMA Players Inputs	0x800001	0b00000010
P2_RIGHT	JAMMA Players Inputs	0x800001	0b00000001
SERVICE	JAMMA Coins	0x800018	0b01000000
P2_START	JAMMA Coins	0x800018	0b00100000
P1_START	JAMMA Coins	0x800018	0b00010000
COIN2_P2	JAMMA Coins	0x800018	0b00000010
COIN_P1	JAMMA Coins	0x800018	0b00000001
DIP1	JAMMA DIPs	0x80001A	0bXXXXXXXX
DIP2	JAMMA DIPs	0x80001C	0bXXXXXXXX
DIP2	JAMMA DIPs	0x80001E	0bXXXXXXXX

6.6.4 Drawing on screen

Requesting tiles to be drawn consists of first describing the layout in GFXRAM, then setting the palettes, and finally writing to the CPS-A and CPS-B registers to point them to "where is the data".

Double buffering

When a frame is being drawn, neither the data in the GFXRAM nor the CPS-A/CPS-B register values can be changed. Raster effects are not possible since HSYNC is not forwarded to the m68k. Changes should only occur during the VBLANKing which is signaled via the `VSync` function.

The proper way to avoid visual artifacts is to double buffer the SCROLL/OBJ descriptors in the GFXRAM. While one buffer is used for rasterization until the next VSYNC, the next frame is prepared in the other buffer. On `VSync` the CPS-A and CPS-B registers are written to swap the buffer roles.

CPS-A and CPS-B registers

The CPS-A registers are always at the same offset in the m68k memory map and they always use the same layout.

Depending on the board being targeted, registers of the CPS-B will move and their internal layout will change. A convenient way to deal with this is to use MACROs and have the build system enable the appropriate ones.

Note that all registers are 16-bit to accommodate the 68000 operating on them. As shown in the summary table, a register offset is always located on an even address.

CPS-A Usage

The CPS-A is controlled via 18 registers.

Name	Offset	Desc
OBJ base	0x00	OBJ GFXRAM absolute address
SCROLL1 base	0x02	SCROLL1 GFXRAM absolute address
SCROLL2 base	0x04	SCROLL2 GFXRAM absolute address
SCROLL3 base	0x06	SCROLL3 GFXRAM absolute address
Rowscroll base	0x08	Rowscroll GFXRAM absolute address
Palette base	0x0A	Palettes GFXRAM absolute address
Scroll 1 X	0x0C	SCROLL1 Offset X
Scroll 1 Y	0x0E	SCROLL1 Offset Y
Scroll 2 X	0x10	SCROLL2 Offset X
Scroll 2 Y	0x12	SCROLL2 Offset Y
Scroll 3 X	0x14	SCROLL3 Offset X
Scroll 3 Y	0x16	SCROLL3 Offset Y
Star1 X	0x18	STAR1 Offset X
Star1 Y	0x1A	STAR1 Offset Y
Star2 X	0x1C	STAR2 Offset X
Star2 Y	0x1E	STAR2 Offset Y
Rowscroll Offsets	0x20	Offsets into Rowscroll base
Video Control	0x22	flip screen, rowscroll enable

CPS-A registers (offset origin is upper-left in screen space)

The base registers tell the CPS-A where it should expect data in GFXRAM. Registers are 16-bit but addresses must be 24-bit so values are expanded `<< 8` upon reception. The linker script should be configured to make sure data structures are aligned properly.

Row Scrolling

Row scrolling allows for offsetting each visible row on SCROLL2 via a discrete X amount. In Street Fighter II, Honda's dohyō (the space in which a sumo wrestling bout occurs) perspective is achieved via linear offset differences. The more perspective needed, the more accentuated the offset slope.

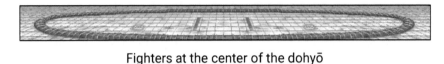

Fighters at the center of the dohyō

Fighters move to the left of the dohyō

Fighters move to the right of the dohyō

To scroll the whole screen, the CPS-A reads 256 values. That is 224 (each visible line) + 16 (one tile height above) + 16 (one tile height below) = 256 values to render a frame.

Each unsigned 16-bit offset value is expected in an array located in GFXRAM and pointed to via the CPS-A register `ROWSCROLL_BASE`.

The `ROWSCROLL_OFFSET` instructs the CPS-A to use values not starting at `ROWSCROLL_BASE` but at `ROWSCROLL_BASE` + `ROWSCROLL_OFFSET`.

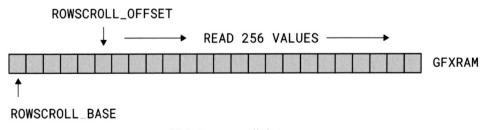

CPS-A rowscroll data access

A convenient trick is to allocate a rowscroll array of size 1024 with one entry for the full height of SCROLL2 to generate all the rowscroll offsets. If SCROLL2 is scrolled vertically, the engine only needs to manipulate ROWSCROLL_OFFSET and no new values are to be generated.

```
GFXRAM ALIGN(256) uin16_t ROWSCROLL_BASE[1024];

// ROWSCROLL_BASE[16]  = first visible line.
// ROWSCROLL_BASE[239] = last visible line.
```

Real-life example

When a contestant in Street Fighter II jumps, SCROLL2 moves vertically but no rowscroll offsets are re-calculated, only ROWSCROLL_OFFSET is moved. This allows to amortize the generation of perspective correct rowscroll offset.

Note that rowscroll offsets are unsigned and always indicate an amount to move toward the left side of the screen. To offset toward the right, Street Fighter II developers took advantage of the wraparound nature of the SCROLL layers and used decalValue = 1024 - desiredRightOffsetValue.

Video Control   This register enables/disables misc attributes.

```
0b00000000_0000001 Enable rowscroll
0b00000000_1000000 Enable Flip Screen 90degrees cw
```

CPS-B Usage

The CPS-B features only seven registers but their location changes based on the version of the chip.

Name	Offset	Desc
Layer control	0x26*	Enable and order layers
Priority mask	0x28*	16-bit mask pen values to draw above OBJ
Priority mask	0x2A*	16-bit mask pen values to draw above OBJ
Priority mask	0x2C*	16-bit mask pen values to draw above OBJ
Priority mask	0x2E*	16-bit mask pen values to draw above OBJ
Palette control	0x30*	Request palette upload

CPS-B registers (*: for Street Fighter 2, CPS-B 11)

Palette control   This register is used to request upload of palette pages, each made of 32 palettes belonging to a same layer.

```
0b00000000_00000001 Upload   OBJ palette page
0b00000000_00000010 Upload  SCR1 palette page
0b00000000_00000100 Upload  SCR2 palette page
0b00000000_00001000 Upload  SCR3 palette page
0b00000000_00010000 Upload STAR1 palette page
0b00000000_00100000 Upload STAR2 palette page
```

Palette upload does not happen immediately. Instead the CPS-A waits until the next VBLANK and starts reading at the address provided via the PALETTE base register.

The CPS-A does not use a fixed base + offset to lookup a palette page. If `SCR1` page is not marked for upload, `SCR2` page is expected immediately after `OBJ` palette page.

Layer control   This register enables or disables a layer individually (with the exception of OBJ which is "disabled" by providing an empty list of tiles). It is also used to define the priority of layers `OBJ`, `SCROLL1`, `SCROLL2`, and `SCROLL3` individually.

Note that STARs are always in the back and in order STAR1, STAR2.

```
0b00000000_00001000 Enable  SCROLL1
0b00000000_00010000 Enable  SCROLL2
0b00000000_00100000 Enable  SCROLL3
0b00000000_00000000 Cannot  control  STAR1
0b00000000_00000000 Cannot  control  STAR2
```

The board studied in this book uses a CPS-B 11 which does not support STAR1 and STAR2. These layers were also marginally used in Forgotten Words and Strider (two good reasons to allow the author to not face his laziness and avoid detailing the STARs bytecode further).

The layer control register is also used to define the order in which OBJ, SCROLL1, SCROLL2, and SCROLL3 should be drawn.

```
0b00000000_11000000 Layer to draw first
0b00000011_00000000 Layer to draw second
0b00001100_00000000 Layer to draw third
0b00110000_00000000 Layer to draw last

Layer IDs: OBJ=0, SCROLL1=1, SCROLL2=2, SRCOLL3=3
```

WARNING : This bit layout changes across versions of CPS-B. What is presented here is for the CPS-B v11. Refer to Mame for documentation on other versions.

> **Trivia:** Starfields were used so little that the bytecode mapper was removed altogether from the CPS-2 API while the ASIC retained its circuits.

Priority mask   These four registers control the precedence of pens belonging to the layer behind the OBJ layer. A tile can be assigned to one priority group within a choice of four ranging within [0-3] . A group tags pens in the tile palette to be drawn with higher priority via a 16-bit bitfield mask. Marked pens a drawn above OBJs pens.

```
FEDCBA9876543210 - Priority Mask bitfield group0
FEDCBA9876543210 - Priority Mask bitfield group1
FEDCBA9876543210 - Priority Mask bitfield group2
FEDCBA9876543210 - Priority Mask bitfield group3
```

TIP : Tiles using priority group often use a palette where "high priority" colors are grouped together. This makes it easy to tag them in the bitfield because the bits are next to each other. e.g: Mask 0xF000 marks pens 15 , 14 , 13 , and 12 as high priority.

Drawing OBJs

To draw sprites and shapes, descriptors must be written to the GFX RAM. Each entry takes four 16-bit WORDS (8 bytes).

```
OBJ entry layout: xxxx yyyy nnnn aaaa
xxxx = x position   (origin upper left)
yyyy = y position   (origin upper left)
nnnn = tile ID
aaaa = attribute word
```

```
// OBJ attribute WORD layout
0b00000000_00011111   Palette ID
0b00000000_00100000   X Flip
0b00000000_01000000   Y Flip
0b00000000_10000000   Unused
0b00001111_00000000   X sprite size (in tiles)
0b11110000_00000000   Y sprite size (in tiles)
```

If the attribute WORD sets the block size to zero, a descriptor commands a single tile to be drawn. Otherwise, the command is interpreted as a Sprite rendering command using block size dimensions.

The CPS-A will stop reading entries from the OBJ descriptors if it reaches an empty entry using attribute value `0xFF00` or if 256 tiles are scheduled for rendition.

WARNING : Sprite commands use only a single entry but every single tile in them count against the 256 tiles limit. There is no way to cheat, this is an hardware limitation, not an API limitation.

Developers do not have to worry about the `STF29` or GFX partitioning. The tileID is relative to the group it belongs to.

Drawing SCROLLs

Rendering tilemaps is much like rendering OBJs. Descriptors must be written to the GFX RAM but the layout is much simpler. Each entry is two 16-bit WORDs wide (four bytes).

```
SCROLL entry layout: xxxx aaaa
xxxx = tileID
aaaa = attributes
```

The attribute WORD is a bit field where we find in particular the palette ID, the group ID which references the priority mask, and the usual X/Y flippers.

```
0b00000000_10000000 Unused
0b00000000_01100000 Priority group (See priority mask)
0b00000000_00010000 Y Flip
0b00000000_00001000 X Flip
0b00000000_00000111 Palette ID
```

All SCROLLs have different size and tile size but they are all considered Sprites (with rectangular dimensions). They all feature 64x64 (4,096) entries.

Scroll name	Tiles Dimensions	Tile size	Dimension
SCROLL1	64x64	8x 8	512x 512
SCROLL2	64x64	16x16	1024x1024
SCROLL3	64x64	32x32	2018x2048

SCROLLs tile size and dimensions

If a full black layer is needed, it can be rendered without using a single tile using either SCROLL or OBJs. Enabling a STAR layer and providing zeroed bytecode does the trick. It renders a STARfield without any stars in it if the CPS-B supports STARfield.

6.7 Back in the Days

The system used by Capcom to program the CP-System remained unknown for many years. Only the nickname of Hiroaki Kondo, a composer/sound programmer often credited as "X68K", alluded to a computer manufactured by Sharp.

In 2018, Akiman confirmed[59][60] that Capcom's SDK, named CAT-1, was launched during the making of Street Fighter II and ran on a Sharp X68000.

6.7.1 SHARP X68000

Unheard of in the rest of the world, the X68000 is a celebrity in Japan where it was nicknamed "god computer". Released in 1987, the first machine in the series was as beautiful and powerful as it was expensive (¥369,000, roughly $3000 in 1987, equivalent to $7,600 in 2022).

SHARP's God Computer. Copyright G-Walk[71]

Despite mind-blowing hardware specifications, SHARP's new product was a risky bet considering it had next to no software at launch. To complicate things further, it used its own text-based OS named Human68k.

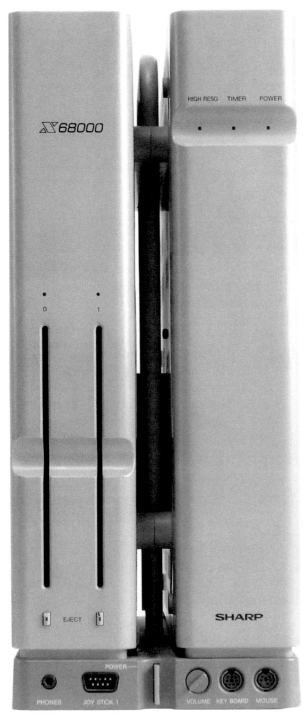

The "Manhattan" twin-tower case of the first model became the signature of the series.

Notice the vertical bar between the two towers. Pushing it down releases a spring to allow the bar to extend past the top of the machine and become a carrying handle.

The ports for the keyboard, mouse, and joystick are conveniently user facing. An audio jack and a volume control are also present.

The two 5.25" floppy drives have elegant motorized "soft" ejection systems.

The three LEDs in the upper right indicates the state of the machine. POWER is self-explanatory, HIGH RESO indicates whether the video output is using 15KHz, 24KHz, or 31kHz, and TIMER indicates if a self-powering is scheduled.

In later revisions, HIGH RESO was replaced with HD BUSY to indicate HDD state.

On the back panel can be found "standard" ports such as additional Line In and Line Out, and an extra Joystick #2 entry.

Images Copyright (left and right): G-Walk [71].

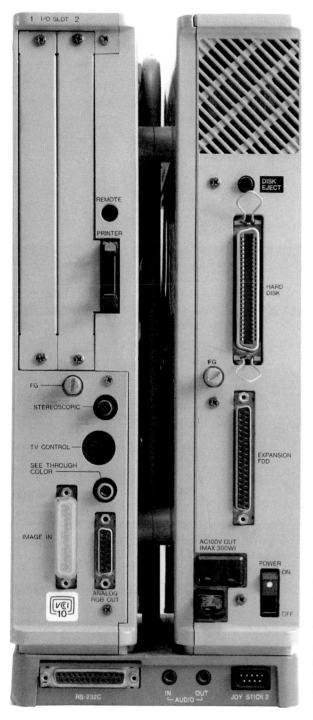

The `TV Control` port drives Sharp monitors and VCRs. It can take advantage of the timer mentioned earlier to schedule a tape recording.

The `See through Color` port is for chroma-keying and roto-scoping.

A `Image In` port is for transferring images from a video device, such as a VCR.

A serial port, `RS232C`, as is found on many IBM PCs.

The `HDD` and `FDD` ports respectively allow Hard-Drive and Floppy-Drive extensions.

The `100V out` outlet provides power for a monitor.

The `Analog RGB out` port is the equivalent a VGA port to carry the monitor signal.

The `Stereoscopic` port drives "shutter style" 3D glasses.

The `Printer` port is a variant of the commonly called parallel port in USA only it is called Mini-Centronics 36-pin.

For everything else, the X68000 features two `extension slots` to welcome extension cards.

Trivia: The two `FG` screws are meant for Frame Grounding since Japanese power outlets lack Ground wire and therefore are not grounded.

6.7.2 X68000 Tech Specs

Inside its gorgeous "Manhattan" case, the machine packed an unparalleled amount of horse power. Even a machine such as the Amiga 500, released the same year and praised in Europe and USA for its prowess, pales in comparison to the X68000.

Type	X68000	Amiga 500
CPU	M68000 10MHz	M68000 7.16 MHz
RAM	1MiB	512 KiB
Max RAM	4 MiB	2 MiB
Colors	65,536 colors (stable)	4,096 (HAM)
Resolution	1024×1024	736x483
Sprite engine	128 units, 16x16 tiles	8 units, 16x16 tiles
VRAM	1056 KiB	-
Sound	Oki MSM6258 (1 channel)	4 channels PCM
Music	Yamaha YM2151 (8 channels)	-
Price	$5,000	$1,500

X68000 vs Amiga 500

If both music and sound capabilities were outstanding, it is in the graphics department that the X68000 made jaws hit the floor.

The 1056 KiB of VRAM are divided into three segments feeding four planes. 512 KiB are dedicated to the Text plane, 512 KiB are for the Bitmap plane and the rest, 32 KiB, are for the joined use of the Background plane and Sprite plane. Each plane can be configured to use distinct resolution and layers.

6.7.3 Video Prowess

The **Bitmap Plane** is particularly well suited to plot pixels and render images. Its direct 16bpp color mode was ideal for raytracing application (a M68881 math coprocessor could be added to reduce rendering time). Four modes are available.

- One 512x512 layer with direct 16bpp colors.

- Two 512x512 layers with shared 8bpp indexed colors.

- Four 512x512 layers with shared 4bpp indexed colors.

- One 1024x1024 layer with 4bpp indexed colors.

The **Text Plane** is deceptively named. It is also a bitmap plane but it expects values across four bitplanes making it well suited to write large quantities of bits in few operations. A m68k writing a 16-bit word can set 16 pixels which makes text rendering very fast when copying characters from a model. Two modes are available.

- One 1024x1024 layer with 4bpp indexed colors.

- Four 512x512 layers with 1bpp monochrome.

The **TileMap Plane** offers two modes.

- Two 512x512, using 8x8 tiles with 4bpp indexed colors (16 palettes).

- One 1024x1024, using 16x16 tiles with 4bpp indexed colors (16 palettes).

The **Sprite Plane** is a sprite layer allowing 128 sprites on-screen (with a max of 32 sprites per scanline). Each sprite uses 4bpp indexed color (16 palettes).

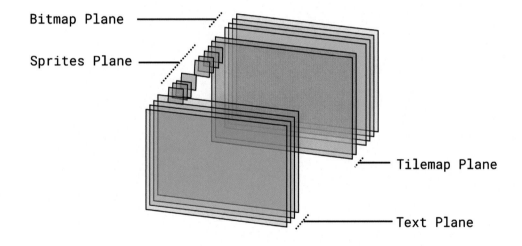

X68000 planes and layers. Copyright G-Walk[71]

In total, if all four planes are used in their most complex form, up to eleven layers can compose the screen concurrently.

An even more impressive feat from the CRT compositor is that all layers of each plane are independently hardware scrollable.

The numerous plane capabilities made the X68000 a versatile instrument able to excel at a wide range of tasks, from simple text editing to demanding raytracing.

Video games were obviously a strength of the machine thanks to its Background and Sprite layers although, as we will see, developers did not employ resources as one would expect.

6.7.4   OS

Developed by Hudson Soft, the operating system named Human68k is strongly inspired by Microsoft's MS-DOS .

All English name commands such as `DIR`, `COPY` and such are available. In fact, Human68k manual is nearly identical to IBM DOS 4.0J manual[69]. The system even uses a `CONFIG.SYS` file to boot.

X68000 OS, Human68k

Several windows-based GUIs running on top of Human68k were released over the years. In succession, "VS" (a.k.a) "Visual Shell" in 1987 and later SX-WINDOW (1989).

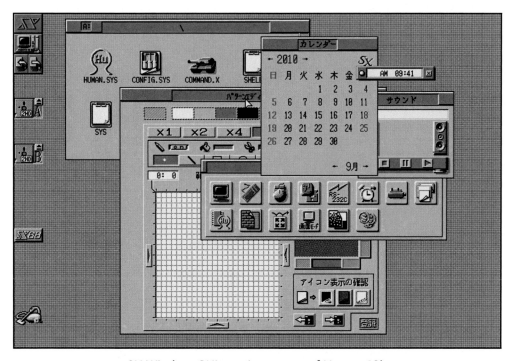

SX-Window, GUI running on top of Human68k

6.7.5   A Development Machine?

The similarities between the X68000 and the CPS-1 are many. A quick glance over the specs on page 210 could easily lead one to conclude that a small layer of emulation is all a X68000 needed to run CPS-1 games, making it a perfect development machine.

Since developers never detailed to what extent SHARP's machine was involved, we can only make an educated guess. A beginning of an answer comes from the hardware components, while Capcom-produced game ports leave no ambiguity.

Hardware response

If the Motorola 680000 CPU and the YM2151 present in both machines are identical, the rest diverge from slightly to significantly.

The sound chip is an OKI but it is "only" a MSM6258. Although it works alike the MSM6296 with ADPCM, it features only one channel which severely impacts how rich the sound effects and music systems can be.

The sprite system is, at first sight, weaker than the CPS-1 since the number of tiles displayable is half (128 instead of 256). But the X68000's access to raster effect allowed multiplexing (the Sprite Doubler by Koichi Yoshida[53]) bringing the upper limit to 512 sprites!

Lastly, the X68000 floppy storage resulted in slow loading time compared to the CPS-1 ROM. To solve this issue, developers used as much RAM as available, going as far as loading the whole floppies during startup if the capacity of the X68000 allowed it.

The 32 KiB VRAM wall

The real issue, and perhaps the only real weakness of the "god computer" is the minuscule amount of VRAM dedicated to feed the Sprite and Tilemap layers. Out of 1MiB, only 32KiB is available which results in asset starvation (it can store only 256 16x16 tiles). This limitation knee-capped any potential of using both layers at the same time. A VRAM shared among layers would have been a totally different story.

Software response

A definitive answer about the viability of the X68000 as a development station comes from Capcom arcade ports.

Game	Year	RAM Requirements
Strider	1992	2 MiB
Final Fight	1992	2 MiB
Street Fighter 2 Champion Edition	1993	2 MiB
Super Street Fighter II	1994	4 MiB
Ghouls'n Ghosts	1994	2 MiB

X68000 Ports of CPS-1 games by Capcom

An analysis methodology shared by Upsilandre[70], leveraging XM6 Pro-68k emulator, shows that the GFX rendering architecture of these titles exhibits no pattern of an emulation layer. On the contrary, the GFX renderers are tailor-made and rely heavily on CPU tricks.

> **Trivia:** The stress on the 68000 is confirmed by Ghouls 'n Ghosts manual which recommends a 16MHz CPU and warns about slowdown on a 10MHz 68000.

All these clues strongly suggest the SHARP X68000 was limited to writing/testing assembly, running TCE, and allocating/compiling the GFXROM for CPS-2 games.

GAME START

DAIMAKAIMURA

● MEMORY USED

This game requires at least 2 MB of memory for each user, so the following models will require additional memory.

> ● **Models that require a RAM expansion :**
> CZ-600C／CZ-601C(ACE)／CZ-611C(ACE-HD)
> CZ-652C(PRO)／CZ-622C(PRO2)／CZ-663C(PRO2-HD)

※ When adding memory to the above models, it is necessary to change the memory used to 2048 with the "HUMAN68K" switch command.
※ Other models have 2MB of memory installed as standard, but it is necessary to check the memory used with the switch command.
※ On the X68030, 4 MB of memory is mounted as standard.

● CLOCK SPEED!

In terms of operation, a 10MHz clock is enough to play, but it may be a little slow in some places.
However, the slowness is not such that the game is not possible.
For a comfortable play, we recommend playing with a clock of 16MHz or higher

> CZ-644C (XVI)   16MHz
> CZ-500C (X68030)16／25MHz

● HARD DISK INSTALLATION

This game can be installed and played on a hard disk.

It is assumed that the hard disk is booted, the hard disk is drive A, and the disks drives are B/C.

1) Start up the hard disk.
2) Create a directory called 'daimakai' in the root directory.
   A>MKDIR A : ¥daimakai
3) Insert the System Disk into drive B.
4) Move to the hard disk directory.
   A>CD A : ¥daimakai
5) Transfer the entire contents of the disc to the hard disc.
   A>COPY B : ¥ *. * A :
6) When you have finished transferring the System Disk, transfer the Data Disk using the same method as in 5).

4

6.7.6 Ports Analysis: Ghouls 'n Ghosts (1994)

Ghouls 'n Ghosts was released in 1994, six years after the arcade version. It is noteworthy for its low RAM requirements of 2MiB RAM and its resolution of 512x512.

It is considered a "perfect port" because of its GFX faithfulness to the CPS-1 version. All the enemies, levels, and weapons are there, rendered with the correct rich colors.

The Tilemap plane is not used at all since the background lives in two software rendered 512x512 Bitmap layers using a shared 8-bit indexed colors palette. The Text layer is also fully software rendered in 1024x1024 16 colors despite the CPU cost of plotting pixels in that mode. The cost and low number of colors makes it a good fit for rendering the GUI elements.

Ghouls 'n Ghosts on SHARP x68000

Notice the vertical "cut" in the right of Bitmap plane Pages 0 and 1. This artifact reveals the wraparound resulting from hardware scrolling these two layers. This technique allows the CPU to render only new portion of the background.

The Sprite layer contains more than sprites. While rendering the wind blowing in the grass only required swapping tile ID on CPS-1, the X68000 could not plot that many pixels in the Bitmap layers. Promoting blades to sprites overlays reduced the fillrate.

The rain effect is replicated as seen on page 95 via the Text layer start offset. Note there is no DMA to/from the VRAM so every single pixel except for the Sprite layer is plotted by the CPU. Thanks to hardware scrolling, that cost is amortized.

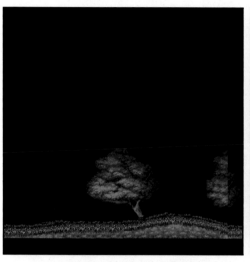

512x512 Graphic Plane Page 0

512x512 Graphic Plane Page 1

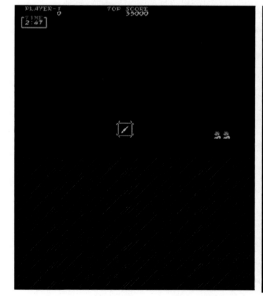

Portion of 1024x1024 Text Layer

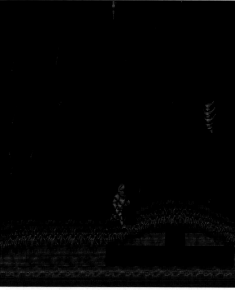

512x512 Sprite Layer

6.7.7   Ports Analysis: Final Fight (1992)

Final Fight was released in 1992, three years after the arcade version. Like the Ghouls'n Ghosts port, the game managed to ship on two 5.25-inch 1.2 MiB floppies.

The graphic render uses the same trade off used by Ghouls 'n Ghosts where usage of Tilemap plane is sacrificed in favor of the ability to feed the Sprite layer with tiles.

Two bitmap layers are used for background elements while the Text layer is used for GUI elements. All these layers are rendered in software with a draw cost amortized thanks to hardware scrolling.

The port of Final Fight to X68000 is close to the arcade version but is not considered "perfect" because of missing graphic elements and color discrepancies.

Final Fight on X68000

The number of characters on screen was restricted to 7 which is less than the arcade version where up to 13 where visible. In this case, both the 32 KiB VRAM and the 128 tiles limits were the limiting factor since no multiplexing was possible with free roaming characters.

The Sprite sandwich trick (page 90), where parts of the staircase appear in front of the Sprite is done with a special blending mode were the MSBs gives precedence over the Sprite layer. This leaves 7bpp for the color indexes and the Background ends up using 128 colors instead of 256. In other levels, this blending mode is not used so the Bitmap layers go back to using 8bpp for a total of 256 colors available.

The YM2151 let music be close to the arcade version but without samples. The OKI6295 is dedicated to playing sound effects on its only channel. These audio shortcomings can be countered via support of MIDI audio playback.

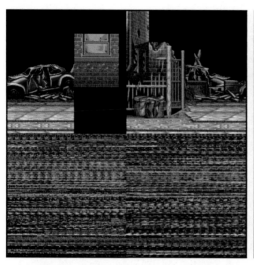

512x512 Graphic Plane Page 0

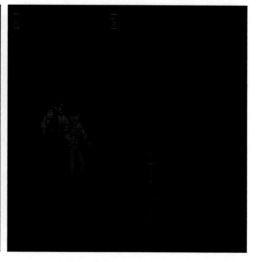

512x512 Graphic Plane Page 1

Portion of 1024x1024 Text Layer

512x512 Sprite Layer

6.7.8 Per Scene Renderer

The color-depth reduction trick is only one among many others. There are many testaments to the hair pulling process an X68000 port appears to be. One of them is the introduction sequence where Damned takes away the mayor's daughter.

The arcade version called for many sprites tiles, among them two heroes, the mini-boss Damned, Jessica, two minions (red Dug and blue Jake), and six barrels. The number of tiles far exceed the maximum 128 sprite tile limit of the X68000.

Final Fight X68000 intro sequence

To manage this problem, developers started by cutting out one minion (blue Jake).

Since it was still too many tiles, they resorted to enabling (for the intro only) the Tilemap plane. Five out of the six barrels are drawn as tilemap in the Tilemap 0.

Since a tilemap is a simple grid of tiles with no concept of sprites and overlap, special 8x8 tiles were generated where columns of barrels are pre-overlapped.

Things get messy when animation must occur. To allow the barrels to be broken into pieces, the engine exploits the timing of enemies fleeing. First when Damned leaves, then when Dug retires, rows of barrels are progressively migrated out of the tilemap layer into the sprite layer.

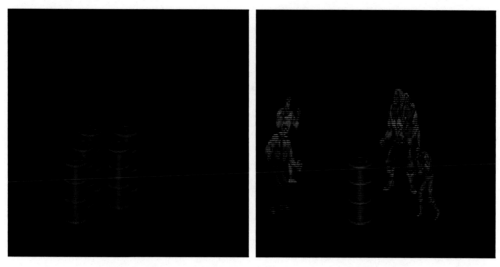

Tilemap 0 Layer   Sprite Layer

The whole trick is not perfect. As the barrels break down, the machine reaches its sprite tile limit. Since the engine is not as elaborated as the arcade version (page 106), a partial Cody is drawn.

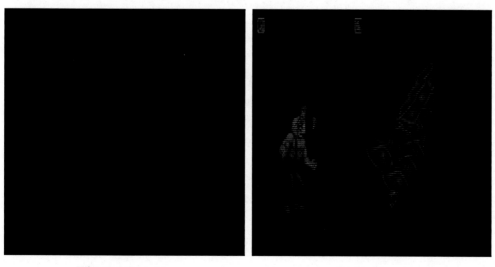

Tilemap 0 Layer   Sprite Layer

6.7.9 Ports Analysis: Street Fighter II Champion Edition (1993)

Street Fighter II Champion Edition was released only a year after the arcade version.

The volume of assets forced the game to ship on four 5.25-inch 1.2 MiB floppies. The game manages to run with 2 MiB or RAM but suffers numerous loading delays when traveling between countries. However, on a machine with 4MiB the game engine loads all floppies to RAM to provide a loading-free experience.

In terms of GFX rendering architecture, the Tilemaps are once again ignored in favor of the Sprite layer. The floors are software rendered. However the per-line parallax is considerably sped up thanks to the combination of raster effect and hardware scrolling. On each HSYNC event the horizontal hardware offset is adjusted which allows rendering Page 0 once and for all.

Some Sprite elements that used to be rendered on the CPS-1 OBJ layer found their way into the Text layer. This layer is not used for GUI but to render decorative sprites (like the statue in Dictator level). It is likely that the 32 KiB was once again not big enough to contain the sprites for both opponents and decorations.

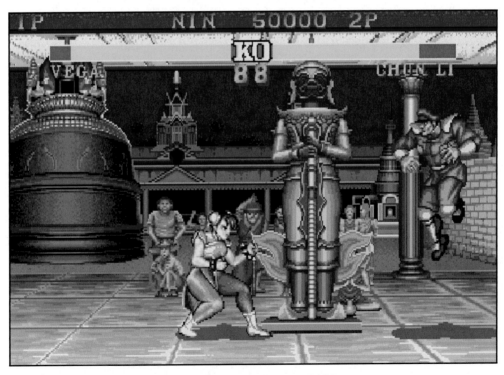

Street Fighter 2 CE on X68000

The 32 KiB VRAM is updated during VBLANK to be populated with the tiles needed on the next frame. The X68000 RAM is used as a Sprite tile Level 1 cache.

Notice the noise in the Graphic layers, the bottom part in Page 0 and the top part in Page 1. The programmers used every avenue possible to store bytes in order to avoid loading from the floppy drives. The parts of the pages not used for composition are used to "cache" background tiles. When the CPU renders, it transfers VRAM to VRAM (sadly without DMA).

512x512 Graphic Plane Page 0

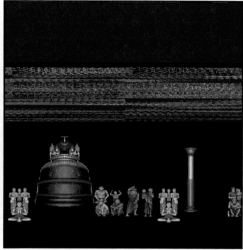

512x512 Graphic Plane Page 1

Portion of 1024x1024 Text Layer

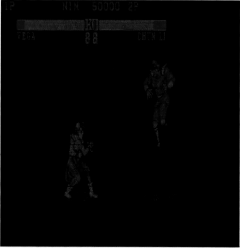

512x512 Sprite Layer

Investigating further into Street Fighter 2: Champion Edition confirms the colossal task required to convert a CPS-1 title to X68000. There were three problems to solve.

1. Find where to store assets.

2. Remain within 32 KiB VRAM per frame.

3. Remain within the m68k software rendering budget

6.7.10   Per Level Renderer

Like in Final Fight, where scenes were optimized on a case-per-case basis, Street Fighter II Champion Edition uses a distinct rendering strategy depending on the arena.

When fighting occurs in China, the Text layer is not used for Sprite decoration like it is in Thailand. Instead it is dedicated to the sky and its animation. Two rows of clouds, accounting for two "frames" of animation are drawn once. The hardware offsets are leveraged to parallax the clouds and alternate their shapes. This was likely done because of the fillrate required to update this layer.

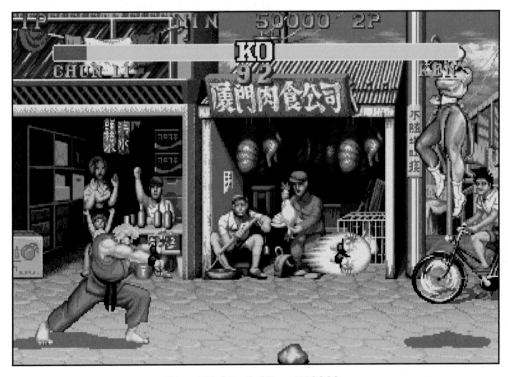

Street Fighter 2 CE on X68000

6.7.11   Saving Further 68000 Cycles

If we look closely at Page 1 and 2, we see that the background is split. The alley is on Page 2 while the rest is on Page 1, which is surprising since no parallax effect exists (they are on the same plane).

This reduces overdraw when the Page 1 cyclist crosses the screen and goes over the other cyclist in the back alley, saving a few CPU cycles.

512x512 Graphic Plane Page 0

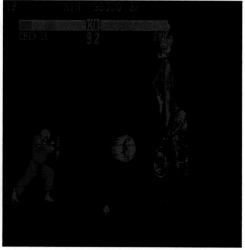

512x512 Graphic Plane Page 1

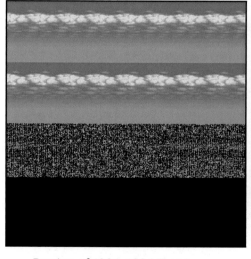

Portion of 1024x1024 Text Layer

512x512 Sprite Layer

6.7.12   The Rise ...

SHARP kept on improving the series with better CPU (68030), more RAM (up to 12MiB) and even bigger HDD (up to 80 MiB). Peripheral manufacturers embraced the computer with extension cards covering anything users and programmers could desire.

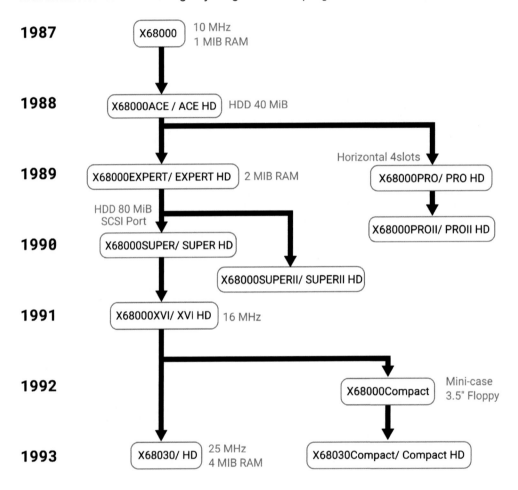

Sharp X68000 series 1987-1993

The risky bet became a phenomenal success. Users loved the platform dearly and publishers released, accounting for games only, no less than 823 titles between 1988 and 1999.

Trivia: The success was such that a magazine dedicated to the X68000, Oh!X, was published from 1988 to 2000 over 139 volumes.

Often featuring a raytraced cover to boast the graphic capabilities of the SHARP marvels, each publication came loaded with software, originally on one, then two, and later three 5.25" floppy disks[61]!

6.7.13   ... and Fall

Ultimately, SHARP updates were too timid to keep up. Even its most recent model sporting a Motorola 68030 CPU failed to remain competitive both in terms of price and performance.

After six years without updating the video or audio pipeline, the 2D oriented design of the machine started to look dated. Other machines found themselves better fitted to embrace an era of 3D started by companies such as Silicon Graphics, 3DfX, and Verity.

In 1993, many felt a great disturbance in the Force. SHARP had discontinued the "god computer".

People

Many people were mentioned during this book. In the early 90s, Capcom arcade division was already large with three teams working on independent titles. It can be tedious to figure out who worked on what. Here is a summary.

Kenzo Tsujimoto, (辻本憲三): Founded Irem in 1974, a company that would go on making many games, including the legendary R-Type and Kung-Fu Master. Forced out over revenues following the release of IPM Invaders (1979), he founded Capcom in 1983 which he led to worldwide success. As of 2022, he is still Capcom CEO.

Poo (Noritaka Funamizu, 船水 紀孝): Joined Capcom in 1985 where he was a planner on CPS-1 titles Forgotten Worlds, U.N. Squadron , Dynasty Wars, and 1941: Counter Attack. He is also credited with "Special Thanks" for virtually every Capcom hit, including Final Fight and all versions of Street Fighter II. He eventually became a General Producer and worked on numerous Street Fighter titles. In 2004, he left Capcom to help found Crafts & Meister.

Akiman (Akira Yasuda, 安田 朗): Joined Capcom in 1985. As a junior artist he was in charge of background on Hyper Dyne Side Arms. After reportedly asking for a promotion in a washroom encounter, he became a planner (focusing on artwork) for Forgotten Worlds, Final Fight, and Street Fighter II. He dedicated himself to artwork for several Capcom titles well after the days of CPS-1. He left Capcom in 2003 and became a freelance artist.

Nin (Akira Nishitani, 西谷 亮): Joined Capcom in 1985. His nickname, "NiN", is well known since it is associated with high-scores in all the games he planned. Among many other titles, he was a planner (focusing on gameplay) on Forgotten Worlds, Final, and Street Fighter II. He left Capcom in 1995 to found Arika and produced the Street Fighter EX series for his former company.

Professor F / Arthur King (Tokuro Fujiwara, 藤原 得郎): Joined Capcom in 1983 and planned Commando, Ghosts 'n Goblins, and Bionic Commando. He became General Manager in 1988. After working at Capcom for 13 years, he left in 1996 to start his own studio, Whoopee Camp.

Kouichi Yotsui (四井浩一): Joined Capcom in 1986 and planned the impressive first CPS-1 title, Strider. He left in 1990 and went on to work at Takeru and later Mitchell Corporation. As of 2022, he works as a freelancer.

Yoshiki Okamoto (岡本 吉起): Joined Capcom in 1984 after leaving Konami. He was a planner on early titles such as Side Arms and Willow before he moved to overseeing all arcade development at Capcom, becoming a producer. He is credited with recruiting Akiman which had a profound impact on the arcade division. He left Capcom to start his own video game development company, Flagship. In later years, he created several successful mobile games such as Dragon Hunter and Monster Strike.

Takashi Nishiyama (西山隆志): Joined Capcom in 1986 coming from Irem where he designed Kung-Fu Master. He was a planner on pre-CPS-1 games, in particular Street Fighter 1 for which he created the special move "Hadouken". He joined SNK in 1990 where he worked on Fatal Fury before becoming a producer on several iterations of King of Fighters and Metal Slug.

Yoko Shimomura (下村 陽子): Joined Capcom in 1988, straight after graduating from Osaka College of Music. She contributed to the soundtrack of over sixteen games starting on console titles before moving to arcades. She is noteworthy for writing the musics of Street Fighter II and Final Fight. She left Capcom in 1993 to work for Square where she is still employed as of 2022.

Yoshihiro Sakaguchi (坂口 由洋): Joined Capcom in 1984. He composed music for both home consoles with titles such as Mega Man and Mega Man 2 and also arcades where he worked on Street Fighter 1 and Final Fight. He left Capcom in the mid 90's.

Epilogue

The CPS-1 study was a passion project that took over a year to complete in my spare time. The goal was to obsessively explore the hardware, understand it down to the metal, and learn how to program it. As is often the case, the journey took an unexpected turn and I came out of the adventure with more than I initially anticipated.

In the beginning, discovering the internals of Capcom's machine was fascinating and borderline addictive. I often found myself in the wee-hours exploring schematics or experimenting with code. The technology that unraveled confirmed the key part it played in shaping Capcom's destiny.

It is when I starting studying the systems competing against the CP-System that my opinion started to evolve.

Capcom's arch-nemesis, SNK, had built an impressive machine which technically surpassed the CP-System. Games were built relying exclusively on sprites without using limiting tilemaps. While the CPS-1 could display 256 sprites, the Neo-Geo could achieve 381. Each of the Neo-Geo sprites could be scaled via a shrinking technique extensively used in successful titles such as Super Sidekicks.

The list of features goes on. Programmers could define animations that the hardware would manage automatically, a feature used profusely in Metal Slug for the gorgeous results that made it famous. HSYNC detection unlocked raster effects. The 330 megabits capacity of its boards was proudly advertised.

Yet, despite hardware's shortcomings, Capcom games were able to hold their own. In several occurrences some even managed to achieve much greater success than titles running on the Neo-Geo. It was as if, past a certain point, technology did not matter that much.

As this book was coming to an end, I found myself admiring more and more the work of the people who infuse life into the silicon. Yes, they had a good platform to work with but it was not a silver bullet either. These creatives slept under their desk. They courageously tracked allocations with paper and scissors, they entered pixel colors by hand, tile by tile, using a keyboard. They worked long nights and passed ROM chips using string through the windows in order to meet deadlines.

This venture started with the goal of giving readers a greater appreciation for the hardware. It ends with an author having opened his eyes to the artists and designers who put a soul in the machine.

- Fabien Sanglard

Appendix

9.1 Making of

This book was written for the most part on a Lenovo X1 Carbon Gen 9 running Ubuntu 22.04. It was a deeply enjoyable experience to work with such a reliable and blazing fast machine.

```
leaf@leaf:~/cpsb$ neofetch
            .-/+oossssoo+/-.
        ':+ssssssssssssssssss+:'
      -+ssssssssssssssssssyyssss+-
    .ossssssssssssssssssdMMMNysssso.
   /sssssssssshdmmNNmmyNMMMMhssssss/
  +sssssssshmydMMMMMMMNddddysssssss+          leaf@leaf
 /sssssssshNMMMyhhyyyyhmNMMMNhssssssss/        ---------
.ssssssssdMMMNhsssssssssshNMMMdssssssss.       OS: Ubuntu 22.04 LTS x86_64
+sssshhhyNMMNyssssssssssssyNMMMysssssss+       Host: 20XW003FUS ThinkPad X1 Carbon Gen 9
ossyNMMMNyMMhssssssssssssshmmmhssssssso       Kernel: 5.10.0-1057-oem
ossyNMMMNyMMhsssssssssssssshmmmhssssssso      Uptime: 2 days, 20 hours, 36 mins
+sssshhhyNMMNysssssssssssyNMMMysssssss+       Packages: 2709 (dpkg), 22 (snap)
.ssssssssdMMMNhsssssssssshNMMMdssssssss.       Shell: bash 5.1.16
 /sssssssshNMMMyhhyyyyhdNMMMNhssssssss/        Resolution: 1920x1200
  +sssssssssdmydMMMMMMMMdddddysssssss+         DE: GNOME 42.2
   /sssssssssshdmNNNNmyNMMMMhssssss/           WM: Mutter
    .ossssssssssssssssssdMMMNysssso.           WM Theme: Adwaita
      -+sssssssssssssssssyyyssss+-             Theme: Yaru-dark [GTK2/3]
        ':+ssssssssssssssssss+:'              Icons: Yaru [GTK2/3]
            .-/+oossssoo+/-.                   Terminal: gnome-terminal
                                               CPU: 11th Gen Intel i5-1135G7 (8) @ 4.200GHz
                                               GPU: Intel TigerLake-LP GT2 [Iris Xe Graphics]
                                               Memory: 2878MiB / 15731MiB
```

A few excursions into Windows 10 territory happened to use Adobe Photoshop when Gimp skills showed their limits.

Source code was synchronized via the awesome Github. LaTeX was authored with Sublime Text 4. Drawings were done with Inkscape. Game screenshots captured with Mame. Compilation was performed by `pdflatex`.

The build system is a custom Golang program able to operate with a single `build.go` command. It takes 1m53s to generate the whole PDF in release mode (300dpi). An incremental debug mode (100dpi) completes within 10s.

The PDF viewer changed between platforms. On Linux, `evince` was used while `SumatraPDF.exe` was chosen on Windows. Both viewers were not only amazingly fast, they also supported auto-reload which was a lifesafer.

All these projects received handsome donations (when they accepted them) for their service.

To remain motivated to ship, a copious amount of moral support was provided by Rudy the cat and my amazing wife Victoria.

Index

Notes & References

[1] **What is a Medal game?** This is not a typo! A medal game is played with metal coins. The most famous ones are "pusher games" where the player must drops coins in a platform system. Each platform moves back and forth as automated brooms. The goal is to push coins groups past the edge of the final platform where they are rewarded to the player.

[2] **What is a Planner?** They were the top decision maker in a Japanese game dev team. Responsible for giving directions and making game design decisions, all other members of the team reported to them. There was usually a single Planner in charge (like Poo on 1943: The Battle of Midway) but there could be two like in Street Fighter II where both Akira Nishitani (Nin) and Akira Yasuda (Akiman) were in charge.

[3] **"1942 Final Review Team Arcade"** (by Tyler Huberty, Greg Nazario, Isaac Simha, link, 2012-09-12.

[4] **"Computer Gamer Magazine #4"** ("Coin-Op Connection" article, link, 1985-07.

[5] **"Questionable figures"**, The figures of "two years and five million dollars" should be taken carefully. These numbers were found on a Forgotten Worlds flyer (28) which also mentioned three Motorola 68000s whereas the final product only included one. 1989.

[6] **"The story of the 3dfx"** (by Fabien Sanglard), link, 2019-04-04.

[7] **"The Sound of Innovation: Stanford and the Computer Music Revolution"** (by Andrew J. Nelson), ISBN: 978-0262028769. 2015-03-06

[8] **"The birth of Chun-Li"** (Akiman for Archipel), link, 2018-02.

[9] **"Computer Speed Claims 1980 to 1996"** (Roy Longbottom), link.

[10] **"Les grands noms du jeu video, Yoshihisa Kishimoto - Enter the Double Dragon"** (Florent Gorges for Editions PixNlove), link, 2012-07-05.

[11] **"Akiman's Twitter"** (akiman), post 1, post 2, post 3.

[12] **"Top 10 Highest-Grossing Arcade Games of All Time"** (Jaz Rignall for us-gamer.net) (200,00 units: SF2 WW sold 60,000 while SF2 CE sold 140,000), link, 2016-01-01.

[13] **"World of Warcraft Leads Industry With Nearly $10 Billion In Revenue"** (Jonathan Leack for gamerevolution.com), link, 2014-26-01.

[14] **"Interview with Noritaka Funamitsu"** (Retro magazine), part 1, part 2, part 3.

[15] **"Mame CPS-1 video driver"** (mame source code), link, 2008-04-11.

[16] **"Mame CPS-1 driver"** (mame source code), link, 2008-04-11.

[17] **"Kabuki z80 encryption"** (mame source code), link, 2008-04-11.

[18] **"Early CAPCOM Arcade Games FGPA"** (Jose Tejada), link, 2020-08-05.

[19] **"Genesis mode H40"** The vertical and horizontal rates in H40 are not the numbers we would get if we were to inject the dot-clock, number of dots, and number of lines in the formulas. This is because the Genesis designers wanted to have the same rate in H32 and H40 modes (59.92 Hz). The dot-clock slows down to 5.37MHz for 28 dots during HBLANK, resulting in 59.92 Hz VSYNC and 15,700 KHz HSYNC (Conversation with Upsilandre).

[20] **"Dot clock rates"** (pineight.com), link.

[21] **"Final Fight Developer's Interview"** (capcom.com), link, 2019-02-08.

[22] **"Street Fighter II Developer's Interview"** (capcom.com), link, 2018-11-21.

[23] **"Capcom Activity Report: Akira Yasuda part 1"** (capcom.com), link, 2016-03-31.

[24] **"Capcom Activity Report: Akira Yasuda part 2"** (capcom.com), link, 2016-04-04.

[25] **"Capcom, A captive audience"** (Robin Hogg & Dominic Handy for The Games Machine, Issue #19), link, 1989-06-01.

[26] **"Yoshiki Okamoto interview"** (Gamest Magazine #38), link, 1989-10-01.

[27] **"Final Fight arcade 2 players"** (arronmunroe), link (Use ',' and '.' to move frame by frame) 2013-10-12.

[28] **"DL-0921 (CPS-B-21) Video Signals Generation"** (Loïc Petit), link, 2020-11-29.

[29] **"DL-0921 (CPS-B-21) Security Scheme"** (Loïc Petit), link.

[30] **"Capcom CPS1"** (Eduardo Cruz), part 1, part 2, part 3, 2015-04-16.

[31] "Capcom Kabuki CPU" (Eduardo Cruz), intro, part 1, part 2, part 3, part 4, part 5, 2014-11-16.

[32] "CAPCOM CPS1 Reverse Engineering" (Eduardo Cruz), link, 2015-06-15.

[33] "CPS1 Project Update" (Eduardo Cruz), link, 2015-09-19.

[34] "Chip Hall of Fame: Motorola MC68000 Microprocessor" (spectrum.ieee.org), link, 2017-06-30.

[35] "Instruction prefetch on the Motorola 68000 processor" (Jorge Cwik), link, 2005.

[36] "CPS-2 Rebirth !!!!" (cps2shock.retrogames.com), link, 2003-04-23.

[37] "We now have a non encrypted version of the encrypted SFZ program ROM" (cps2shock.retrogames.com), link, 2000-12-32.

[38] "Mame CPS-2 Driver, keys (cps2crpt.c)", link.

[39] "Street fighter 2 WW glitch invisible dhalsim" (youtube.com Error1), link, 2010-09-22.

[40] "Blending Worlds With Music: Interview With Composer Yoko Shimomura" (otaquest.com), link, 2019-12-26.

[41] "Programmer's Guide to Yamaha YMF 262/OPL3 FM Music Synthesizer" (Vladimir Arnost), link, 2019-12-26.

[42] "CPS-B Number" (tim for arcadecollection.com), link.

[43] "The Untold History of Japanese Game Developers Volume 1 (Interview: Koichi Yotsui)" (John Szczepaniak), 2015-11-04.

[44] "Game Maestro #4", link.

[45] "Street Fighter 2: Oral History" (Matt Leone), link. 2014-02-03.

[46] "Blending Worlds With Music: Interview With Composer Yoko Shimomura" (OTAQUEST Editor), link. 2019-12-26.

[47] "BEEP! Megadrive magazine: The Women of Game Making" (translated shmuplations.com), link. 1990-10.

[48] "Unfinished Strider Conversion" (Shoestring), link. 2016-02-17.

[49] "How to Phoenix a CPS 2 PCB" (Joe Bagadonuts), link. 2015-05-18.

[50] "Dialogic ADPCM Algorithm" (Dialogic Corporation), link. 1988.

[51] **"Street Fighter 2 Manual"** (Capcom Corporation), link. 1992.

[52] **"Street Fighter 2: The AI engine"** (Ben Torkington), link. 2017-1-20

[53] **"X68000 Sprite management"** (Koichi Yoshida), link. 2021-02-25

[54] **"How To Make Capcom Fighting Characters"** (Akiman, Kiki, Bengus), ISBN: 978-1772941364. 2020-010-20

[55] **"Akiman, 2003 Interview from Capcom Design Works"** (Akiman, translated shmuplations), link. 2003

[56] **"A Talk Between the Creators of Street Fighter and Fatal Fury: KOF"** (Yoshiki Okamoto and Takashi Nishiyama), link. 2021-08-09

[57] **"Street Fighter II Complete File"** (Capcom edition), ISBN: 978-4257090014. 1992-11-15

[58] **"Shoryuken..! The music of Street Fighter II"** (909originals), link 2021-21-02

[59] **"The CPS-1 SDK, a.k.a CAT-A"** (Akiman), link 2018-07-01

[60] **"The CPS-1 SDK, a.k.a CAT-A: Additional details"** (Takenori Kimoto (a.k.a KimoKimo)), link 2018-07-02

[61] **"Private View:** 月刊電脳倶楽部 **(GEKKAN DENNŌ CLUB)"** (Ted Danson), link 2015-06-25

[62] **"MSM6295 datasheet"** (by OKI), link

[63] **"Sony SMC-70 Microcomputer"** (by Ahm), link 2011-05-19

[64] **"Capcom – Retrospective Interview"** (by https://shmuplations.com/), link 1991

[65] **"Street Fighter II Interview Soundtrack OST"** (Yoko Shimomura), link 2017-10-28

[66] **"Diggin' In The Carts, Hidden Levels"** (conversation Yoko Shimomura with Manami Matsumae), link 2014-09-23

[67] **"Street Fighter II Platinum Source Code"** (Ben Torkington), link 2021-10-10

[68] **"Japan's Technical Standards: Implications for Global Trade and Competitiveness"** (John Mcintyre), ISBN: 978-1567200539. 1997-02-28

[69] **"Human68k Manual"** (gamesx.com), link 2019-08-27

[70] **"Le x68000 et la supériorité japonaise"** (upsilandre), link 2020-12-04

[71] **"X68000 Perfect Catalogue"** (by G-Walk), ISBN: ISBN4867171018. 2020-10-27

Made in the USA
Middletown, DE
22 May 2023